INDIANS

POCAHONTAS, *Seymour*
SACAGAWEA, *Seymour*
SEQUOYAH, *Snow*
SITTING BULL, *Stevenson*
SQUANTO, *Stevenson*
TECUMSEH, *Stevenson*

NAVAL HEROES

DAVID FARRAGUT, *Long*
GEORGE DEWEY, *Long*
JOHN PAUL JONES, *Snow*
MATTHEW CALBRAITH PERRY, *Scharbach*
OLIVER HAZARD PERRY, *Long*
RAPHAEL SEMMES, *Snow*
STEPHEN DECATUR, *Smith*

NOTED WIVES and MOTHERS

ABIGAIL ADAMS, *Wagoner*
DOLLY MADISON, *Monsell*
JESSIE FREMONT, *Wagoner*
MARTHA WASHINGTON, *Wagoner*
MARY TODD LINCOLN, *Wilkie*
NANCY HANKS, *Stevenson*
RACHEL JACKSON, *Govan*

SCIENTISTS and INVENTORS

ALBERT EINSTEIN, *Hammontree*
ALECK BELL, *Widdemer*
CYRUS MCCORMICK, *Dobler*
ELI WHITNEY, *Snow*
ELIAS HOWE, *Corcoran*
ELIZABETH BLACKWELL, *Henry*
GEORGE CARVER, *Stevenson*
GEORGE EASTMAN, *Henry*
HENRY FORD, *Aird and Ruddiman*
JOHN AUDUBON, *Mason*
LUTHER BURBANK, *Burt*
MARIA MITCHELL, *Melin*
ROBERT FULTON, *Henry*
SAMUEL MORSE, *Snow*
TOM EDISON, *Guthridge*
WALTER REED, *Higgins*
WILBUR AND ORVILLE WRIGHT, *Stevenson*
WILL AND CHARLIE MAYO, *Hammontree*

SOCIAL and CIVIC LEADERS

BETSY ROSS, *Weil*
BOOKER T. WASHINGTON, *Stevenson*
CLARA BARTON, *Stevenson*
DAN BEARD, *Mason*
FRANCES WILLARD, *Mason*
JANE ADDAMS, *Wagoner*
J. STERLING MORTON, *Moore*
JULIA WARD HOWE, *Wagoner*
JULIETTE LOW, *Higgins*
LILIUOKALANI, *Newman*
LUCRETIA MOTT, *Burnett*
MOLLY PITCHER, *Stevenson*
OLIVER WENDELL HOLMES, JR., *Dunham*
SUSAN ANTHONY, *Monsell*

SOLDIERS

ANTHONY WAYNE, *Stevenson*
BEDFORD FORREST, *Parks*
DAN MORGAN, *Bryant*
ETHAN ALLEN, *Winders*
FRANCIS MARION, *Steele*
ISRAEL PUTNAM, *Stevenson*
JEB STUART, *Winders*
NATHANAEL GREENE, *Peckham*
ROBERT E. LEE, *Monsell*
SAM HOUSTON, *Stevenson*
TOM JACKSON, *Monsell*
U. S. GRANT, *Stevenson*
WILLIAM HENRY HARRISON, *Peckham*
ZACK TAYLOR, *Wilkie*

STATESMEN

ABE LINCOLN, *Stevenson*
ANDY JACKSON, *Stevenson*
DAN WEBSTER, *Smith*
FRANKLIN ROOSEVELT, *Weil*
HENRY CLAY, *Monsell*
JAMES MONROE, *Widdemer*
JEFF DAVIS, *de Grummond and Delaune*
JOHN MARSHALL, *Monsell*
TEDDY ROOSEVELT, *Parks*
WOODROW WILSON, *Monsell*

David Farragut

Boy Midshipman

Illustrated by Robert Pious

David

Farragut

Boy Midshipman

By Laura Long

THE **BOBBS-MERRILL** COMPANY, INC.
A SUBSIDIARY OF HOWARD W. SAMS & CO., INC.
Publishers • INDIANAPOLIS • NEW YORK

To
Philip William Long, Jr.

Illustrations

Numerous smaller illustrations

Contents

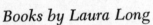

Books by Laura Long

DAVID FARRAGUT: BOY MIDSHIPMAN
GEORGE DEWEY: VERMONT BOY
OLIVER HAZARD PERRY: BOY OF THE SEA

★ # David
Farragut

Boy Midshipman

Stony Point

It was spring and the two boys, James Glasgow and William, were helping their mother plant garden. The woman was on her knees, making a proper seed bed with a trowel.

"We'll be having fresh vegetables soon," she said to the boys. "Aren't you getting tired of squash and potatoes?"

"I like turnips, Mother," said William, "and little green onions." He was remembering the gardens of other summers.

James Glasgow was only two, which is too young to remember. He held out his hand to his mother. "More seed," he said.

She poured the tiny black seeds into his open palm. They were too busy to hear the footsteps of the man and woman who came through the gate a few minutes later.

"Is this where Captain George Farragut, the ferryman, lives?" called the stranger.

The boys' mother got up from her knees and brushed the earth from her fingers. "Yes, but he's not here," she said.

"Papa gone fishin'." James Glasgow smiled his best smile at the strangers.

"Will he be back soon?" asked the man. "I would like for him to ferry us across the river. We're moving to Nashville, ma'am. There would be the two of us, and our horse and our cow and our wagon."

Glasgow brushed the seeds from his hand and ran toward the river. His father's boat was not at the landing. He ran back to his mother.

"I'll have my boy call him," his mother was

saying. "William, go blow the horn for your father, please."

James Glasgow trotted after his six-year-old brother, up the hill and into the cabin. William took the silver horn from the hook over the fireplace. Then he ran down the hill to the rocky point that was like a high shelf over the river. James Glasgow ran after him.

William put the horn to his lips and puffed out his cheeks. He blew with all his might.

James Glasgow reached for the horn. "My turn now!" he said.

William tried to push him aside. "You're too little. He'd never hear you."

"He would too!" said Glasgow.

The boys could see their father's ferryboat down the river. It was standing almost still, while Captain Farragut fished.

William started to blow the horn a second time, but Glasgow hung on his arm.

"My turn! My turn!" he cried. He was close to tears, he wanted so badly to blow the horn.

"All right!" said William finally. "It's not so easy as it looks."

Glasgow took a deep, deep breath and blew the air through the horn with all his strength. It made a loud, shrill sound that Glasgow thought was quite perfect.

The boys waited, watching their father's boat. After a moment came the high, sad sound of the boat horn.

"I knew he'd hear!" said James Glasgow.

The boat came into the landing.

"Movers!" called William. "Will you take them, Father?"

"May I go?" called Glasgow.

"Tell them I'll take them," the captain said to William. "Though why they have to come bothering me just when the fish are biting—!"

The boys ran to tell the movers. Glasgow

started to follow the strangers back to the ferry. There was nothing he liked so well as crossing the Holton River on his father's ferryboat.

His mother called him back. "Glasgow, you can't go!"

"Why?" asked Glasgow, unhappily.

"We're not through planting garden! When you start a thing, you must stay with it until it is finished. Suppose I ran off after I'd started making a garden! We'd never have any fresh vegetables that way!"

Glasgow was tired of the garden. He wanted to go with his father, but he let his mother fill his small hand with seeds. He carefully dropped them into the shallow bed she had made with her trowel. Then William covered the seeds with fine warm earth. In a short time they would have a nice garden.

Stony Point, called Campbell's Station by some, was in Tennessee, on the north bank of

16

the Holton River. The Farraguts had lived there ever since Captain George Farragut had brought his bride there from North Carolina.

Captain Farragut had been born on the island of Minorca near Spain. He had been a restless boy, and finally he ran away from home to go to sea. That was how he had happened to come to America. He had fought for American freedom in the Revolutionary War. Now he was an officer in the militia. He was a brave man and a gay man, always ready for adventure. His boys loved him very much.

Sometimes Captain Farragut took the boys with him on the ferry. Sometimes he took them fishing. The whole family liked the water. Sometimes the captain made the boys stay at home with their mother.

"We can't leave her alone, boys," he would say. "The Indians might come while we're gone."

The Farragut cabin lay halfway between two

Indian warpaths. The Cherokee trail was east of them, the Chickasaw west of them. The Creek Indians lived across the Holton, to the south. Sometimes the boys would see half-naked savages wandering through their woods. Once they had seen a grinning, dark face pressed close to the window of their cabin.

Glasgow was four when a party of Indians did come. They pounded on the cabin door. Elizabeth Farragut motioned for the boys to be quiet. She took her husband's gun from the corner and stood close to the door.

"Go to the attic!" she whispered to the boys. "Crawl under the bed. Wait till I call you. Not a sound out of you, remember!"

They were more afraid of the look on their mother's face than they were of the Indians. They hurried to do as she told them.

They lay on the attic floor, listening. They heard the Indians knock again. The boys were

18

curious. They scooted along the floor until they could look down through the square opening that had been cut for the ladder. From there they could see into the room below.

"Will you go if I give you a present?" they heard their mother ask the intruders. They could not hear what the Indians answered, but they could see their mother unlatch the door and open it wide enough to hand out the gift.

Suddenly Mrs. Farragut screamed. Glasgow screamed, too, but he didn't know why. The boys saw their mother slam the door quickly. They saw her leaning against it, as though she could not stand alone. Only then did they remember that they had seen something whiz through the air. Something lay on the floor by the door—an Indian hatchet.

They forgot what their mother had told them, and hurried down the ladder. Glasgow fell down the last two rungs because he was so eager to run to his mother and hold fast to her wide skirts. There was blood dripping from his mother's wrist.

"Go get me some spiderwebs," she said. Her face was white. The blood was very red.

The boys climbed the attic ladder again. They climbed on top of their beds. They pulled themselves up on the rafters. There, close to the roof, they found some spiderwebs. It was the only place in a house as clean as Elizabeth Farragut's that spiderwebs could be found. They held their hands far apart and tangled the webs in their fingers. The feel of the webs made Glasgow shiver, but he held them tightly.

The boys came down the ladder slowly, leaning their shoulders against the sides, their hands full of spiderwebs. There was nothing so good for bleeding as spiderwebs, even not very clean spiderwebs, they knew.

Mrs. Farragut covered her arm with the webs.

Then they all watched. Soon the wound on her arm had stopped bleeding.

"There!" said Elizabeth Farragut. "It's all right now." She began to cry. The boys began to cry, too. Glasgow felt better then. It was as though the danger was over, and he could be just a little boy again. The Indians were gone. Soon his father would be home.

When Captain Farragut came and heard what had happened, he took up his gun to go after the marauding Indians.

"Please don't be so foolish!" cried Elizabeth. "What chance would you have alone against a whole war party? If you must go, get others to go with you."

"It will be too late then," the captain objected. He did as Elizabeth told him, though. The whole neighborhood hunted Indians all that day. Never again did an Indian stop at the Farragut cabin.

A Long,
Long Voyage

In 1807, when Glasgow was six years old, the
Farraguts moved to New Orleans. America had
bought the Louisiana Territory from France a
few years before. A friend of Captain Farragut's
had been made governor of the territory. Governor Claiborne wanted the captain to help him
make Louisiana Territory American instead of
French or Spanish, as it had been before. Captain Farragut was to help get rid of the river
pirates who were stealing American shipping.

Captain Farragut had been a Spaniard and
was now an American. He spoke and understood
Spanish. So did all his family.

"*Buenos dias!*" Glasgow would say, when he came down from his attic room in the morning. When he went to bed at night, he would say, "*Buenas noches!*" When his mother would call to him—if she was afraid he was in mischief— "Glasgow, what are you up to?" he would answer, "*Nada*, Mamma, *nada!*"

Then his mother would hurry to see what he called *nada!* For *nada* means nothing, and it was not very often that Glasgow could be found doing nothing at all.

As soon as Captain Farragut decided to move to New Orleans, he began building a flatboat on which to move his family and their possessions. From the time the ice first melted in the river, the boys and their father worked on the boat. A young man who had come from Kentucky also helped. The boat was to be ready for the fall freshets, when the rains came.

Glasgow knew every plank nailed to that flatboat. He himself had helped whittle the wooden pins that fastened the planks together. Each day he felt prouder of it.

One day his father came home with a letter. Governor Claiborne needed him right away. He could not wait until the boat was finished. The young Kentuckian would have to finish it alone and bring the Farragut family to New Orleans in the autumn. The captain was leaving at once.

All that summer the two boys helped build the flatboat. William could saw the lumber, but Glasgow was not old enough to pull the squeaking saw through the hard wood. Glasgow rubbed oakum, thick as tar, over the sides of the boat, to keep it from leaking.

One day late in August they went down to the boat. That day not even the Kentuckian could find anything more to do to her. "I reckon she's ready to go," he told the boys. "We can put off as soon as there's a really good freshet."

24

The next day it rained. The day after that it rained. The day after that it rained. Glasgow had never enjoyed the rain so much. Then the sun came out, and the air was hot and steamy, especially along the river.

Elizabeth Farragut, loading her household things on the boat, wiped her red face on her apron. "The hottest place in all creation is a flatboat in the summer!" she complained.

The boys took off their long shirts and jumped into the river to cool off. They felt happy. Tomorrow they would start for New Orleans!

It did not stay hot forever. Before they finally arrived in New Orleans a friendly wind had hurried their boat through the water. Too, an unfriendly wind had tried to upset them. Once their wagon wheels, which were lashed to the railing, were blown loose and rolled into the water. The boys had to hold their noses and dive under the water to find the wheels.

Before the end of their voyage they had been baked by the sun and chilled by the wind. They had been soaked by the rain and shut in by a fog so thick they could scarcely see one another. Toward the end of their journey there was even a light snow.

It had been fun at first.

"The boat is our floating house," Glasgow had said.

Soon it was too small a house, though. They ate and slept and cooked and bathed in the one little room that was their cabin. There was only one cabin. The four oarsmen and the young Kentucky pilot lived and slept on the open deck, no matter what the weather. Sometimes they slept on shore, on the bare ground. Sometimes the boys slept on shore with them.

It was not safe for a boat to travel at night. Great trees grew in the rivers. At night they were invisible. Too, there were river pirates who were said to come out of hiding in the dark. Many travelers had been killed or captured by these men. Still more had been robbed.

The boys kept hoping they might see some of those pirates.

"Why do you want to see pirates? I certainly don't," said the young Kentuckian.

"Papa says they speak Spanish," Glasgow said. "I want to talk to them."

What he really wanted was some slight change from the empty days of river travel, something exciting. There was nothing to do on a flatboat, and nothing to see, and nowhere to go. Every day was like every other day, nearly.

"Look, Glasgow! Indians!" William would call to him, pointing. Glasgow's heart would leap, even when he was almost sure that William was only fooling him.

"Look, Glasgow! People!" William would call. It was only another Indian village. They

had passed several. There were no white towns,
not even a little settlement. They saw Indian
boys their own age playing with light canoes in
the river. They watched them swim with a feeling of envy. The Indian boys could swim better
than the Farraguts could.

"Halloa!" Glasgow called to the swimmers.

"Ayah! Ayah!" the boys called back. They raised their dark arms in greeting. One of them pointed his little bow at the flatboat but the little arrow fell short of its mark. Glasgow grabbed his bean shooter and squinted his eye as he aimed, but the bean hit the water and skimmed along like a tiny white boat.

"If we hadn't been moving, I could have hit him!" said Glasgow. "It's harder to aim straight when you're moving."

The Holton River met the Tennessee River and the Tennessee met the Ohio. It was more interesting on the Ohio. There were more boats. The boys could call out to the people on the other boats and it was less lonely. They traveled forty miles on the Ohio before the Ohio met the great Mississippi.

After that, even the four boatmen began to talk about river pirates. The boys sat with their wooden guns pointed, watching for pirates.

Finally they saw some queer men in an old boat. One had a black patch over his eye. Another had no right ear.

"Likely got it chawed off in a fight sometime," said Juan, the oarsman, as though this were nothing. "Boys, them's your pirates."

William and Glasgow felt disappointed. The pirates didn't even look at the flatboat.

"What would they want with us?" asked the oarsman. "They're looking for something valuable. Only cargo we got is young'uns. Young-'uns ain't worth a whoop."

The boys forgot about pirates when they saw the New Orleans harbor. It was crowded with boats of all kinds—sailing ships, keelboats, and even a steamboat.

Their father was waiting for them. He was wearing a new uniform. Glasgow thought he looked wonderful.

Captain Farragut kissed his wife and his

children. When he had kissed them, he counted them. One, two, three, four—they were all there. William was ten years old, Glasgow six, Nancy three and a half, George barely old enough to toddle.

At Christmas time the Farragut family welcomed a new baby to their home.

The Big Blow

CAPTAIN FARRAGUT'S work was to cruise along the Gulf and up the bayous of the Mississippi hunting for slave ships and smuggled goods. Sometimes he took the boys with him.

One morning they were to go with their father across Lake Pontchartrain. Glasgow wakened early and looked out the window. The long shutters were thrown back to let in the warm, heavy, moist air.

It was a clear day, and already warm. By noon it would be really hot. He looked at the sky. The sun was a big red ball.

Glasgow started to dress. He called William,

and he looked at the sky again. His mouth grew dry with dread. Now the sky was red! Red suns were unlucky for sailors. Everyone knew that.

"Red sun in the morning,
Sailor, take warning!"

Glasgow said the words over three times, more alarmed each time.

"Papa will go anyway. A red sun won't stop him," Glasgow told his brother.

William nodded. "The more danger, the better he likes it."

Glasgow thought his mother must have seen the red sun, too, for as they were leaving she put her hand on his shoulder. "Your father won't let anything happen to you. Don't worry, son," she whispered.

It was easy for his mother to say that. She didn't have to be in a hollowed-out boat as unsteady as a canoe, in the middle of a big lake when a storm was coming.

They were hardly settled when the wind freshened. The boat was so low it seemed to Glasgow that they were sitting on top the water, with waves roaring straight at them. The lake seemed almost as wide as the world to him. The wind rocked and rolled the boat from side to side.

The red sun had warned them!

The wind was tormenting the boat more and more. The captain's gun rolled from one side of the boat to the other. The captain tried to balance the boat by having the boys add their weight to the side farthest out of the water.

"Port side, boys! Port side!" he called. In the same breath he changed to "Starboard, now! Hurry! *De prisa! De prisa!*"

The boys, ordered to hurry in two languages, scrambled wildly from one side to the other.

34

Glasgow felt queer. He kept on feeling more queer. He had never felt worse in his whole life. He was seasick, and his fear made him sicker. He lay down flat in the bottom of the boat, moaning softly. His father and William were too busy to pay attention to him.

The wind spun the boat around like a top.

Glasgow heard a man call to his father. "Captain Farragut! Hadn't you better come aboard till this blow is over?"

Glasgow sat up. They were close to a Navy schooner that was riding the storm out with her sails pulled in. It was a small schooner but it seemed as big as a warship to Glasgow. He looked at his father hopefully. He should have known better.

George Farragut was never a man to seek safety. He enjoyed fighting the wind. He only laughed at the man on the Navy boat. "I've been in much worse blows than this!" he yelled.

Glasgow sighed and lay down again. The man on the schooner tried to argue. "Maybe you have, but not in that boat. Come aboard before we have to fish you out of the water!"

The captain laughed. Glasgow felt more sick.

"You won't have to do that!" he heard his father call. "I once sailed clear to Havana in a boat like this. That was really dangerous, but I made it safely."

There was a fresh blast of wind, and a white-capped wave broke over the side of the boat. Glasgow felt the cold water on his bare feet.

The boat rocked and turned. William tumbled from port to starboard, trying in vain to outguess the wind.

Suddenly the wind died. The waves were not so high now. Soon the lake grew smooth again. It was late afternoon then. The storm had delayed them for hours.

"See?" said Captain Farragut. "Such storms

often blow up over Lake Pontchartrain. I told you we'd be all right."

Glasgow soon felt better. He was no longer seasick. However, he was ashamed that he had been frightened. He should not have doubted his father.

They crossed the lake at last and the boys helped their father pull the boat up on shore. The captain spread some spare sails on the wet ground. This would be their bed. Their bed-covers were more sails.

"Say your prayers!" ordered Captain Farragut. "Get on your knees and thank the good God for making our little boat stronger than His great wind. You don't have enough faith. I knew all the time He'd see that we made it."

"You mean a red sun doesn't mean anything?"

"*Nada*," said George Farragut.

Too Much Sun

GLASGOW thought William had all the luck. William was twelve, and had a midshipman's commission, and would be leaving soon to go to his ship. William belonged to the United States Navy and would learn to be an officer.

"We ought to go fishing again before William leaves," said Captain Farragut.

"Let's go today," Glasgow said.

"It's hot today," the captain said, "but it may be hotter tomorrow."

"Are we going today?" asked Glasgow.

"Yes," said his father.

They met another fishing boat on the lake. The

men on it were Navy men also, but the Farraguts' catch was three times as much as the other boat's. Captain Farragut always knew where the fish were, thought Glasgow proudly.

"It's like hunting for pirates," said the captain. "You have to know where to look for them."

Glasgow was almost as good a fisherman as his father. He let one big fellow get away, though, because he was too small to land it. The next time he felt a tug on his line he asked his father to help him. Even William was proud of Glasgow when he saw a big fish flopping in the bottom of the boat—but William didn't admit it.

"Bet you can't do it again," said William.

They had stopped fishing to eat. They were finishing the sandwiches Mrs. Farragut had made for them when someone from the other boat called to Captain Farragut.

"Come aboard, George! Something has happened to Captain Porter!"

Captain Porter had been in charge of the other fishing party. He was an old man who had been in the Navy many years. He had a son in the Navy. The son was away at sea.

Glasgow went with his father. William stayed behind to watch the fishing lines. The old sea captain lay still on the deck.

"Is he dead?" Glasgow whispered.

His father shook his head. "Sunstroke," he said. He turned to the others. "Captain Porter needs a doctor. I'll take him back to town."

They put the old man on a stretcher and let him down into the Farragut boat. Back in New Orleans the boys and their father carried the stretcher home. The doctor came.

"He'll not live long," said the doctor. "He must have constant care."

"I'll see that he has it, as long as he needs it," said Elizabeth Farragut. "He is my husband's very good friend."

Glasgow liked Captain Porter. He liked to listen while the captain talked of old days in the Navy. The old gentleman loved to talk.

The day William left for his ship, Captain Porter talked more than ever. He understood that the boy left behind would feel lonely. So he went through all his life's best adventures for Glasgow's benefit.

"I mind when I was master of the 'Eliza'—" he began. At twilight he was still remembering old adventures.

Elizabeth Farragut lighted the lamp. "Go do your chores," she told Glasgow. "You'll wear Captain Porter out with so much talk."

"Just one more question!" Glasgow begged. "Did you ever have to serve in the British Navy? Did the British ever board your ship and make you go with them? You were born in England, weren't you?"

"Aye, and I was impressed. Twice," said the

old man. "Both times I got away—but not before I'd learned a few things from the British that came in handy years later. Wherever you are, you can learn something."

Glasgow doubted this. "Not when you have to stay home," he complained. He was still feeling the sting of his brother's leaving.

"Why not? You look about you and then come and tell me what you've learned."

That night when Glasgow had finished his chores and eaten his supper, he went to the old man's room.

"I had to bring in wood from the woodpile," he told the captain. "Some of the wood had been there so long it had rotted, but the cypress wood, no matter how old it was, was still sound. Pine doesn't rot, either. Cypress is harder, and oak is the hardest of all. I've learned that."

"Good!" the captain said. "What else?"

"When I make a fire in the fireplace, I set fire

first to some kindling. I blow on it, just a little, to make it burn. If I blow hard, the fire goes out, but if I blow just a little, it burns better."

"You're beginning to learn at last," said Captain Porter. "See that you keep it up."

"I will, sir," Glasgow said. "It's fun."

That autumn the old captain's son, Captain David Porter, came back to New Orleans. He had finished his sea duty. He came to take care of his father, but by the time he reached New Orleans, the young captain had a dreadful disease called Asiatic cholera. Half of New Orleans had the cholera that winter. Many people died from it.

Elizabeth Farragut was one of those who died of the cholera that terrible winter. She was ill only a few days.

A friend of the family's had promised to care for the children until their mother grew better. She had never grown better. No one told the Farragut children that their mother was dead. Yet somehow Glasgow knew it. He felt sure that something terrible had happened to them all. He felt he would never again see his mother. He begged to go home, but no one paid any attention to him.

The day after the funeral, Captain Farragut came for his children. Then he told them about their mother. Glasgow said he had known it for days. Captain Farragut thought he must have overheard someone talking, but Glasgow said he had known it, without hearing it.

He had not guessed, though, that on the same day his mother had died, old Captain Porter had also died. He felt surprised and shocked when he heard this. He had not been surprised when he heard about his mother. He had sensed it all the time.

Captain Farragut brought his children back home. He hired a woman to look after them.

Glasgow thought it was no longer home, now that his mother was not there. The place smelled of sulphur candles. He hated the smell of them.

He missed his mother. He missed William, who was still at sea. Even his father was not the same. Captain Farragut was no longer gay. He looked sad. He didn't laugh heartily, as he used to laugh.

At night Glasgow would cry himself to sleep. He had never before known what it was to be lonely. He knew now.

"I don't want to stay here!" he would sob. "I want to go to sea. I want to go now!"

"I Want to Go"

When young Captain Porter was well, he came to see Captain Farragut. "My wife and I have been discussing a plan," he said. "We want to help you, as you and your wife helped my father. We want to take one of your motherless children to raise as our own, sir."

Surprised, the captain said, "I don't know. Any one would be hard to spare."

He looked at the baby, named for her mother. No, not Elizabeth. Nancy climbed on his lap and patted his cheek. Not Nancy. He looked at his namesake. Not George. Finally he looked at Glasgow. He shook his head.

"I need them all," he said. Then he remembered that Captain Porter could do more for a child than he could afford to do. He thought of young Mrs. Porter. A child needed a mother. He turned again to his children.

"Which of you wants to go live with the Porters?" he asked gruffly.

"I do," said Glasgow, so quickly it even startled himself. The rest of them looked surprised.

"I hardly know what to say," George Farragut said. "Are you sure, Glasgow?" he asked. "You would be leaving us all forever."

Glasgow wasn't quite sure. There was something he had to know first. "May I be a midshipman, like my brother? May I go to sea soon?"

Young Captain Porter smiled. He put his hand on the boy's shoulder. "When you're old enough," he promised.

"He's only seven," said Captain Farragut.

"Couldn't I go any sooner?" Glasgow asked.

"We'll have to see," said Captain Porter.

Glasgow looked at his father. "I want to go, Father," he said.

When the new housekeeper had brought his clothes packed in a sea chest, and when he had kissed the baby and Nancy, he wasn't sure. His father put his arms around him and kissed him on both cheeks, in the Spanish fashion. Glasgow felt tears in his eyes.

"He'll make a good Navy man," he heard his father tell Captain Porter.

"Are you ready?" asked the young captain.

Glasgow swallowed. He grabbed his father's hand and held it against his face. He threw his arms about his father's neck.

"Papa! *Adios*, papa! *Hasta luego!* Next time you go across the lake or up through the bayou, take me with you!" he cried.

"You're Captain Porter's boy now, son. I can't take you with me."

"Of course you can!" Captain Porter said. "Any time! I want to help you, not rob you."

Glasgow felt better. He kissed his father's hand, as Spanish children did, and turned to Captain Porter. "Well, Captain," he said, "everything is shipshape. Shall we weigh anchor?"

The young captain smiled. "Aye, aye, sir! All's well."

As Glasgow walked up the street, he could fairly see himself in midshipman's uniform. If he had stayed with his father, he could not have been a midshipman. One midshipman's commission was enough for one family. Now he was sure he would get his commission, too. That was why he wanted to go.

This was the first time he had felt good since the day his mother had become ill.

They walked in silence to Captain Porter's quarters on St. Peter's Street. Captain Porter opened the iron gate.

"Here we are, Glasgow. I hope you'll be happy with us." He called to a woman who sat in the courtyard, reading. "Dear, I have brought you a son to raise!"

The lady got up and came toward them. She kissed her husband lightly and stooped to shake hands very solemnly with Glasgow.

"Welcome home, Glasgow. If you wanted to come as much as we want you, everything will be wonderful."

Glasgow thought it was already wonderful.

Later, there were times when he was not so sure. Captain Porter was sterner than Captain Farragut. He was used to training boys on a warship, where obedience was important.

"Glasgow, do as I tell you, and do it now!" the captain would thunder. His tone was enough to frighten a boy into obeying.

Sometimes Glasgow would argue. "But you see, sir, you see, it's this way——"

"*Glas*—gow!"

"Yes, sir. Right away, sir!" Glasgow would murmur, as he hurried off to obey.

The captain's pretty wife was kind but even less understanding. She did not yell at Glasgow, but she could never understand why a boy would be attracted to dirty little streams of waste water that flowed down the center of the New Orleans streets. Why would a boy want to sail fleets of paper ships down those filthy streams? Why must he so often smell of that sour, green, sloppy water? He might get some kind of fever. Yet he seemed amazingly healthy.

He was still constantly asking his favorite question. "When can I be a midshipman?"

"When you're old enough. I've told you a hundred times, Glasgow!" Captain Porter would answer impatiently.

The young captain often took the boy with him while he, too, hunted for pirates and runaway slaves. Glasgow had been with his father enough to know how to find all the favorite hide-outs for smuggled slaves and for pirates. The captain found the boy surprisingly helpful.

Glasgow was learning. He knew how the Mississippi River emptied into the Gulf of Mexico. He knew how the five outlets of the river were like the five fingers at the end of a broad arm. He knew that in early spring the watery fingers grew choked with the winter's mud, changing the river bed until a boat was in danger of running into a mudbank. He knew that sometimes the spring rains washed part of this mud into the Gulf and changed the shore line. He knew the forts on the high ground guarding the turns in the river, overlooking the Gulf.

Captain Porter's search for pirate ships was finally successful. At last he found one! Glasgow would have given his two front teeth, which were loose anyway, to have been along when it happened. As luck would have it, that day he had stayed at home—and all because of a bit of trouble he had had with his foster mother, for having launched a new fleet of paper boats in an open sewer! He had promised he wouldn't, but he had forgotten. He had been punished.

He had to content himself with the captain's account of what happened.

"We waited in hiding, and saw her run out and capture a small Spanish vessel. We thought she'd be filled with Spanish gold by the time we got to her. We were right! We took her by surprise. Now that we have her, we don't really know what to do with her."

Captain Porter wrote the Navy for orders and was directed to come to Washington. He would go the long way round, by way of Havana, Cuba. He was being transferred from New Orleans and would probably go to sea again.

The captain explained this to Glasgow. "Are

you sure you want to go with us? No telling when you'll next see your father. You can't even tell him good-by."

"I told him good-by last week, before he left on a government mission," said Glasgow. "I'll go with you—unless I'm old enough for a commission."

"So you're going," said the captain. "That much is settled. Your mother will go by stagecoach to Washington. You had better go with her, I think."

"How are you going?" Glasgow asked.

"On the bomb ketch, 'Vesuvius,'" said Captain Porter.

"Why can't I go on the 'Vesuvius'?"

"You can, I suppose, if you want to. You'll have to work, though."

"I'll work," Glasgow promised.

The first thing Glasgow had to learn on the "Vesuvius" was how to climb the yards to the top of the masts. The ship had two masts. The main-mast was almost in the center of the vessel, to leave room in front for the bombs. It seemed to Glasgow that the masts ran halfway to heaven, and that the wind always started blowing a gale when he started climbing. Captain Porter taught him always to climb from the windward side, so that the wind would blow him against, and not away from, the mast. He was so little that he had to hold very tight, to keep from being blown into the sea.

"Remember what I tell you now," said the captain. "If you're not careful, you'll be blown away and no one might ever know it."

Glasgow shuddered. However, he always remembered the captain's teaching. He remembered to be very careful.

At Last!

THEY WERE to be in Washington for several months. "You'll be in dry dock for a while, Glasgow," teased the captain. "No water, no ships— think you can stand it?"

Glasgow was doubtful.

"He can go to school," Mrs. Porter said. "Have you ever been to school, Glasgow?"

"No, ma'am."

Moreover, Glasgow didn't think he would like it. He didn't. The other boys read out of books. He didn't know how to read. When he stumbled over a word, they laughed. He gave them plenty of chances to laugh, too.

Finally he grew tired of their laughing. "Maybe I can't read or write," he cried, "but I know things none of the rest of you knows. I've been to Havana, Cuba. I've hunted pirates and smuggled slaves. I've taken a spell at the wheel when no one else was looking. I can hold onto the royal yards in a bad blow and not be blown to sea."

They didn't know what he was talking about, but they were interested. He had to explain that the wheel was the helm of a sailing ship, by which it was steered, that the royal yards were the very top part of a mast.

"You can't add three and three, though," the master pointed out.

"I know important things like larboard from starboard and lee side from weather side. Do you know one from the other, sir?" asked Glasgow politely.

"I'm afraid I don't."

After that the other boys liked him. They

asked him so many questions about the sea that he began to strut with importance.

Still he could not write his own name. He was beginning to want to learn, though. That was something.

Finally, though he bit his tongue almost in two and raised a blister on his finger, he managed to write, plainly enough for even Captain Porter to read it:

J. G Farragut

This display of learning was followed by his usual question. "Can't I go to sea? I can write my own name on the book now."

The captain sighed. He was tired of answering that question.

One morning a few weeks later Glasgow offered to show the captain again how much he was learning.

"I can write my name better now. Want me to show you, sir?"

The captain was busy. "Not now. I must hurry. I have an appointment with the Secretary of the Navy this morning."

Glasgow's eyes opened wide. "Let me go with you," he begged.

"No, you must go to school."

"I want to write my name for him, so he'll see I'm old enough now to go to sea."

Captain Porter smiled. Then he gave up. Maybe this would put an end to the boy's constant questions. Let the Secretary himself tell Glasgow he wasn't old enough. Maybe the boy would believe him.

"You must promise me that you will not open your mouth until we have finished our business," said the captain.

Glasgow promised—but he would ask a question when they were through talking business.

He kept his promise. He waited outside the Secretary's office until Captain Porter called to him to come in.

"Now you can ask Secretary Hamilton your question, Glasgow."

Glasgow stood by Captain Porter's chair, the captain's hand on his arm. Captain Porter introduced him to the Secretary.

"This is my adopted son, Mr. Secretary—Glasgow Farragut. Glasgow, this is the Secretary of the Navy. What did you want to say to him?"

Suddenly Glasgow's mouth felt dry. He wanted to run away—and yet he wanted even more to ask his question. He looked down at the carpet and rubbed the toe of his shoe along a crack in the floor board.

Then he looked up and the shyness left him. "I'd like to have a commission in your Navy, sir," he said. "I want to be a midshipman."

Secretary Hamilton looked at him. He motioned for him to stand beside a high desk by the window.

"Why, you don't quite come to the top of that desk, boy! How old are you, anyway?" he asked.

Glasgow was ready for that. "I was born on the fifth of July, eighteen hundred and one, at Campbell's Station, also called Stony Point, Tennessee. That's real near Knoxville, sir. My father, George Farragut, knows Mr. Andrew Jackson well. My father is Spanish, but he fought for America in the war. He was a major in the Tennessee militia, and now he's a captain, sir, in your Navy. My brother——"

Glasgow stopped suddenly. It had just occurred to him that it might not be a good idea to mention William's commission at the same time he was asking for one for himself.

"So you're only eight years old!" said Secretary Hamilton. "A midshipman ought to be fifteen or sixteen, you know."

This seemed unbelievably old to Glasgow. "I can write my name," he boasted. "I can write it real good, though it takes me awhile."

Both men laughed at this.

"Keep on going to school for a few years more, Glasgow," advised the Secretary. "Then come and talk to me."

Glasgow knew that meant he had lost. He

would try again, anyway. Maybe, if he could make the Secretary smile a little——

"The master I go to was an officer in Napoleon's army, sir. What does an Army man know that a Navy man doesn't know better?"

"The boy certainly has sense," said the Secretary, laughing again, "but he doesn't have years enough yet."

Captain Porter put his hand on Glasgow's red hair. "The Navy's his calling, that's certain. He's a regular river rat, Mr. Secretary. He knows more about sailing than many a post captain. I'd be willing to wager that his country will be proud of him someday."

Secretary Hamilton looked at Glasgow. "Let's make a bargain," he suggested. "You promise to go to school regularly until you are ten. Then, on your tenth birthday, if Captain Porter will agree to look after you, I'll see that you get your commission."

This was better! Not so good as Glasgow had hoped, of course, but certainly better than having to wait until he was fifteen or sixteen! He held out his hand to the Secretary.

"Gentlemen always shake hands on a bargain, sir," he said.

Solemnly they shook hands.

Then Captain Porter said, "We must go. We've taken up too much of your time now."

Secretary Hamilton did even better than he had promised. Even before Glasgow's ninth birthday, Captain Porter received orders to go to Norfolk, Virginia, to take command of a ship called the "Essex." He was to get the "Essex" ready to go to sea.

They went to Norfolk by stagecoach. When they were settled, Mrs. Porter reminded Glasgow of his promise to Secretary Hamilton. "School again, Glasgow!"

"I've got to help get the ship ready!"

This time Captain Porter agreed. "He'll be going with me when I leave. The older boys will have had years of training. He can be useful. The chaplain is having classes for the midshipmen. He could go to them."

"But he's not a midshipman. Also, he's not ready yet for midshipmen's classes."

Glasgow went back to school for a while. Outside of school hours and every day during vacation he worked on the "Essex." The minute school was out, he signed his name on the ship's book—a better signature this time.

J. G. Farragut

He worked from April till June, when the paymaster handed him thirteen silver dollars.

"I wish it was pieces of eight, instead of dollars," Glasgow said.

"What will you do with it?" asked Mrs. Porter.

He smiled and said nothing—but he knew. A few days later he stopped to have a chat with the captain's tailor.

"I'm to get my commission soon," he said. "I want you to make me a uniform. I want it made just as well as Captain Porter's."

The tailor looked at him and laughed. "Hm!" he said. "It'll be like working on doll clothes."

He made two uniforms, a dress uniform and an everyday uniform. Glasgow thought he looked wonderful in them.

"Now I'm ahead of William," he said. "I'll have my commission when I'm nine years old. William was more than twelve."

Mister Farragut

CHRISTMAS of 1810 was a Christmas Glasgow would never forget. His commission, dated December 17, was his best present. There could be none better, he was certain. He was sorry now that he hadn't given more of his time to reading, for he could not read the print on the official papers. Captain Porter read it all to him. It sounded fine and important.

"You can read your own name, can't you?" asked Captain Porter. He handed Glasgow the official document.

Even his own name looked strange to him. Instead of the familiar *J. G. Farragut* there was a word that looked like the captain's name, instead of his own.

David Glasgow Farragut

That was the name he saw. He looked up at the captain. "Haven't they got it wrong?" he asked. "Haven't they given me your name instead of my own?"

"I told them that was your name. I want you to have it. If I had a son of my own, I'd call him David. Well—you are all the son I have, David. So that's the name I am giving you."

David Glasgow felt proud of his new name. There was no name he would rather have than the captain's.

"I—I don't know how to say it," he stammered. "I—well, it's a name I can always be proud of. I'll try never to make you sorry you have given it to me, sir."

"That's enough thanks for me," Captain Porter said. He reached in his pocket then and took out a little chamois bag. He handed it to Glasgow. "Here," he said. "Look inside."

Glasgow untied the string on the little bag. He looked inside. He took out the gold watch he saw there. He looked up at the captain. "She's a beauty," he said. "Is she—did you get her for Christmas?"

"Open the watchcase," said the captain. "See how good you are at reading."

Glasgow opened the case and saw the engraved initials: D. P. to D. G. F., U.S.N., 1810.

He felt happy, but the only thing he could think of to say was, "Holy mackerel!" So he said that over and over. "Holy mackerel! Holy mackerel! Well, holy mackerel!"

Captain Porter was smiling. "My own father gave me a watch when I received my first commission. I'm doing the same for you, son."

"Well, blow me down! I wasn't expecting all this, sir," said David Glasgow Farragut happily.

That year he went to all the holiday parties with his foster parents. He wore his new uniform for the first time. He looked very grand, he was sure. His dress uniform had a coat with blue tails, just like Captain Porter's dress uniform. It had diamond-shaped squares of gold lace on each side of the standing collar. The slashed sleeves had three little gold buttons on them. His vest and breeches were white, as were the captain's. His shoes had gold buckles and his cocked hat was trimmed with gold lace.

He was the talk of Norfolk. He was so small and so very grand and he walked with such a swagger that people couldn't help smiling. The girls were delighted with him.

"Isn't he cute?" they said.

"He looks like a boy doll," said one. "Only he isn't so pretty. In the face, I mean."

"Ask me for a dance, Mister Farragut!" each one begged of him.

Glasgow strutted more whenever he heard his new midshipman's title. He was having a wonderful time. He picked the prettiest girls for his partners. It was a happy holiday season.

Captain Porter signed up his crew for the "Essex" that winter and by midsummer the ship was ready to join Commodore Rodgers' coast squadron. Congress had passed an Embargo Act that kept American vessels from going far from their own coast. It was hoped that keeping American ships at home would prevent a war with both France and England. It didn't prevent a war, but it did delay it a little. It also nearly ruined the Navy. Nobody wanted to be in a Navy that never went to sea.

It was a hot, sultry day in mid-August, in the year of 1811, when Captain Porter took official command of the "Essex." David Glasgow followed him up the gangplank. The "Essex" guns fired their salute of honor for the captain, and the drums beat four ruffles. Glasgow felt very proud.

Everyone was coming on board at once, and everything seemed in confusion. Yet everyone seemed to have time to smile at the little midshipman who stood at attention, chest out, chin almost pressing against his spine. Suddenly the confusion ended. Everyone was at his own station. Captain Porter was standing before them, speaking, starting from this first moment to make them into a smoothly working unit. They were the men of the "Essex," with the same aims, the same loyalties, the same devotion to duty.

The captain stood on the quarter-deck, with his officers grouped about him. The midshipmen were in front, where they could see all that was to be seen. In front of them all stood the youngest midshipman. He was watching, with solemn brown eyes and tight lips and wildly beating heart, everything that was going on about him. He heard the crew, gathered on the spar deck, repeat the words that would make them from this day on a part of the United States Navy. He heard Captain Porter read aloud the orders from the Secretary of the Navy.

The "Essex" would sail along the coast, as part of Commodore Rodgers' squadron. The men grumbled among themselves good-naturedly as they heard this. They would have liked something far more exciting, but orders were orders.

"There's to be big doings later," said the rumors.

The youngest midshipman felt his throat tighten as he watched the flag of the United States raised and saw its red and white stripes take the wind. Then up went the captain's own flag, and the men cheered. Glasgow felt the pressure of the new watch the captain had given him. He was wearing it under his uniform, and it seemed to have more value since the captain was both his commander and foster father.

The ship's band struck up a lively tune and soon the men were all singing together. David Glasgow Farragut's heart was full of a fine new feeling of devotion to the "Essex" and a new and greater affection for Captain David Porter, whose name he bore. He had just promised to give his country his deepest loyalty and devotion and to serve with all his ability in his country's Navy. Never had he been more deeply moved. Deep in his secret heart, he was offering his life to his country's Navy. It was a new and important feeling.

Suddenly a boy's voice called out crossly, "*Mister* Farragut! Douse the gab! A man can't hear himself think, with all your babble!"

Mister Farragut looked around. He had been too excited to talk since he'd been aboard. The fellow couldn't mean him—but he had said Mis-

ter Farragut. Maybe—well, maybe his brother William was on board. He looked around again, half expecting to see his big brother.

The tall, thin boy who had called to Glasgow now grabbed him by his new coattails. Then he tossed him high in the air, like a rubber ball. Another midshipman caught him and tossed him back. He was too surprised to call out. Then he remembered the captain's warning.

"If the big boys bother you, show fight. If they get the idea they can worry you, they'll do it. Put a stop to their hazing before they start it."

Glasgow grabbed the first boy's blond forelock and pulled. He kicked at anything within reach of his heels. He was a small whirlwind.

The boys hadn't expected this. They thought they could frighten him. They let him go, gladly. One boy held his hands over his stomach, where Glasgow had kicked him.

There were fifteen midshipmen on the "Essex."

They were all ages and sizes. They were all equal, though—but they had to win their right to be equal. Even the weaker ones had to prove they were strong. Glasgow wasn't weak, but he was little. He was the youngest of all.

The other boys saw what was happening. They loved a fight. They laughed when Glasgow kicked the big boy in the stomach, but when the two started for Glasgow, they shouted.

"Fair fight or not at all!"

"Two against one's not fair!"

"Not when they're both bigger!"

"One at a time, Mister! Take your turn. Who wants this ball of fire first?"

They made a circle, eager to see the first real excitement since they'd come aboard.

Mister Farragut was doing very well when Captain Porter looked in that direction. The captain came and stood on the outer rim of the circle. The boys coughed and sneezed, to warn the fighters, but the fighters could not hear them. They went on fighting.

Finally the captain reached for his young ward's torn coattails and lifted him over the heads of the boys in the circle. He stood Glasgow on his feet, and put his hand on his shoulder.

"Gentlemen!" he called.

Fifteen—no, fourteen, for Glasgow was too startled to remember—fourteen midshipmen stood at attention and saluted their captain.

"This is my young aide, Mister Farragut," said the captain. "I want you to know him. I shall expect him to be treated as befits his rank. I hope you will keep him contented while he is on board. Anyone who torments him without good reason will have to answer to me. Remember that. Remember that "Essex" men do not abuse those younger and weaker than they are."

"I'm not weaker!" wailed Mister Farragut. "I'm stronger than those two put together!"

The captain went on talking. "Whoever starts a fight with one who is smaller or weaker than he is, is a bully. I'll have no bullies on board the 'Essex.' "

The captain walked away. No one said a word for a minute, and then everyone seemed to talk at once. Some of them looked with approval at Mister Farragut.

"He's as game as a bantam rooster," said one.

Another came to him and put his hand on his shoulder. "You're a regular firecracker, Mister Farragut. Not much for size, but mighty explosive. If this bunch gives you any more trouble, come to me. The name is Ogden, sir— *Mister* Ogden, *Mister* Farragut."

"Thank you, Mister Ogden. I'll not be needing your help, though," boasted Mister Farragut. "I can take care of myself—but it's decent of you to offer."

A Time to Fight

THE "ESSEX" was Glasgow Farragut's home for three years. Her officers were his family, her crew his friends. Family and friends together numbered several hundred men and boys, and, of them all, Glasgow was youngest.

This was both good and bad. The older men would overlook his faults. If they found him asleep on watch, they would not waken him. They would not punish him. They would cover him with a blanket and pretend they had not seen him asleep on duty. It was the other way around with the midshipmen. They granted him no favors. Instead they made him do all sorts of things they disliked doing. They wouldn't let him be idle a second. They kept him running from duty to duty. Glasgow didn't mind. No one really mistreated him.

The midshipmen slept on the gun deck, which was the middle deck. They slept in hammocks. Except for hammocks instead of beds, it was like a large dormitory. They were a noisy crowd, lively and good-natured.

No one had a minute alone. If four sat down for a quiet game, four more would be rolling on the floor in a wrestling match. If one boy tried to write a letter home, a half-dozen others would pick that moment to sing a chantey.

Midshipmen were busier than any officers. They were supposed to do all the things their superiors didn't like doing, in addition to all their regular duties. Their piping voices repeated the commands of the older officers from their stations in different parts of the ship.

"All hands man the braces!" the captain would order, when the wind sharpened suddenly.

Then Glasgow's childish voice could be heard calling out, as loudly as it was able, "All hands man the braces!"

"Heave back the main-topsail!" the captain would call, when a visitor asked to come aboard.

Glasgow would start the command by crying it at the top of his voice. His companions echoed it. "Heave back the main-topsail!"

Glasgow was glad that Captain Porter had taught him how to climb the yards to the royals, the very top of the mast. He liked to climb up high, high, and higher, when a storm was brewing. He didn't know it made the men below ashamed to be afraid, to see so small a boy so fearless in a strong wind.

Glasgow soon believed that the favorite command of every officer who even looked at him was "Away aloft, there!"

His small size helped him climb. He could climb faster than any of the boys. He was as sure-footed as a cat. He was not afraid of falling, because he knew how to hold on. The captain had taught him how to keep his balance among the ropes of the rigging that moved and held the sails.

The farther aloft he climbed, the better Glasgow liked it. He could see clear to the sun, and to where the endless sea met the endless sky. He liked it up there, away from the others. It was quiet, and he could think his own thoughts. He liked the feel of the wind on his cheeks, in his hair. It seldom blew too hard for him. He liked to sit on top of the mainmast, watching the sea change in color, feeling the wind change, far above the noise of the ship and the constant commands of the officers. The sea understood him. No one else understood him so well, not even the captain, whom he had learned to call the Old Man.

The "Essex" cruised along the coast. Whenever they came near Norfolk, the captain went ashore. Mrs. Porter still lived in Norfolk. Glasgow would have liked to go home with the captain, but that was against rules. He must stay on board with the others, except for an occasional shore leave. Then Mrs. Porter would cook all his favorite dishes, and do what she could to please him. He didn't really like shore leave so much as he had expected. At home he was a little boy again. On the "Essex" he was an officer in the United States Navy.

Glasgow, as captain's aide, had charge of the small boat that took the Old Man from ship to shore. This boat was called a wherry. One morning he stepped down into the wherry to go ashore, to bring the captain back to the "Essex." It was a beautiful day. The sun was bright and the air was crisp and fresh. The wherry had never looked neater. Neither had he, he knew. He ordered the oarsmen to stand in close to shore and wait for the captain to come on board. While they waited, he stood in the bow.

Mister Farragut knew only too well that he made a fine figure standing there. It pleased him to see the idlers on shore look at him, and then smile as they went by. He stood with his head high, his chest out. He held his small curved sword with its hilt against his chest, its blade pointing upward. The gold lace on his cocked hat sparkled in the bright sunlight.

Any boy who looked so neat and grand, who stood so straight and proud, who handled his sword so expertly, was bound to run into trouble sometime. Midshipmen were taught from their first day on ship that they were never to pick a fight on shore, never to hunt for trouble. However, trouble came sometimes without hunting.

There was a gang of Norfolk boys around the wharf that morning. They took one look at Mister Farragut. It was more than they could stand. They began to laugh and point in his direction. They made fun of his grand manner. They pranced along the water's edge, their noses in the air, their stomachs instead of their chests thrust forward. They waved sticks instead of a sword. One of them waved a large water pitcher that he was carrying.

Mister Farragut pretended he did not see them. He was obeying orders. He was not looking for trouble. One of the oarsmen stood in the bow close beside Glasgow, holding the wherry close to shore by a large boat hook. The oarsman couldn't help laughing at the boys on shore, but he laughed to himself. He didn't let Mister Farragut catch him at it.

Then the boy with the pitcher dropped to his knees and scooped up the dirty water close to the shore. Quickly he stood up and tossed the pitcherful of filthy water on Mister Farragut's shining uniform. His gold-trimmed hat was dripping.

Mister Farragut's grand manner began to crumble—but he didn't forget that he was in command of the captain's wherry.

"The boat hook!" he ordered. "Grab him by his breeches, matey!"

The oarsman laughed and swung the boy with the pitcher into the air and dropped him down in the wherry. The boat hook was still caught in the boy's breeches. The boy was screaming and kicking with fear. He was no match for Mister Farragut, who began to strike at him.

"I'll teach you to have proper respect for the Navy! I'll teach you to have a care how you treat its officers!"

Finally the thoroughly frightened boy rolled over the side of the boat and swam ashore.

"Let him go," said Mister Farragut, when the boatman took fresh hold of the boat hook. "He's learned his lesson."

The boy had friends on shore. They had hurried to the shore police as soon as they saw what was happening. The police came on board and arrested everyone on the wherry. They were about to take them all to the Norfolk jail when Captain Porter arrived. Everyone started talking at once, trying to tell the Old Man the things that had happened.

Finally, when everyone had spoken, the captain looked at Mister Farragut. He was not pleased with him. "I am ashamed of you," he said. "You knew better."

By that time Mister Farragut was ashamed, too—but he was not ready to admit it.

"Shore boys will always be envious of midshipmen. They are sure to torment them. You don't need to fight back, though. There's a time to fight, and a time to pay no attention to insults. In the Navy you've got to know one time from the other."

"This was the time to fight, sir," said Mister Farragut sadly.

"It was not," said the captain. "You know it was not, Mister Farragut."

He turned to the shore police. "I'm sorry it happened. You can see the boy's pretty young.

92

However, it isn't your duty to punish my offi-cers. I'll see to that myself."

"That suits us," said the shore police. "We don't want any trouble."

Mister Farragut didn't get to shore again for a month. He didn't like that. One day, though, Mister Ogden told him something he had heard the captain say to Lieutenant Downes.

"I wish I could have seen that fight," said Mister Ogden. "I heard the Old Man tell Lieutenant Downes about it. He said you were three pounds of uniform and seventy pounds of fight. That's a lot of fight for a boy your size. He said he was proud of you. The other fellow was twice your size."

"They're all twice my size," Mister Farragut complained. "Can I help it, though?"

He didn't mind being punished now. The captain was proud of him. Well, he was proud, too, if the captain was!

A Stormy Christmas

CHRISTMAS of 1811 was Mister Farragut's second Christmas spent in uniform. His first had been spent with the Porters in Norfolk. His second was to be on the "Essex," just off Newport, Rhode Island.

"A bit of good luck that is," Mister Ogden told him. "There are no better officers' parties anywhere than at Newport."

"Can anyone go to them?"

"Anyone that's invited."

"Are you invited?"

"All the 'Essex' officers are invited."

"Me, too?" asked Glasgow.

"You're an officer, aren't you? Not a word was said about size in the invitation—pint-size like you is just as welcome as a hogshead like the second mate."

"The girls all liked me at the holiday parties last year in Norfolk."

Mister Ogden groaned. "Yes, I remember," he said patiently. "You've told me all about it. Several times, in fact."

"I'd better try on my dress uniform," Mister Farragut said. "I may have grown some."

He had grown more than he thought. The vest wouldn't button at all. Even when he sucked in his breath and held it, the buttons wouldn't quite meet the buttonholes. The trousers were two inches too short. Maybe he wouldn't be as popular as he had been last year. Maybe the ladies would laugh at him.

"I'll quit eating sea pie for breakfast and plum duff for supper," he told Mister Ogden.

"That'll never do it," said Mister Ogden cruelly. "I'm taking the first watch to shore. See you later, Farragut."

It was Christmas Eve. The first watch went ashore just at twilight. When Mister Ogden brought the boat back, he reported a change in the weather.

"It's getting as cold as Greenland," he said. "All that's going ashore had better go right away, or they'll never make it. You can hardly see through the snow now."

The men couldn't leave their watch, though. By the time they were ready to go, the weather was worse than ever.

"A thick snow and a thicker fog and a wind like a knife cutting through you," someone said.

"Wear your flannels!" Glasgow called. It was still not his turn to go. He would go in the morning—Christmas morning. It was his duty to waken the dogwatch at four o'clock.

"The masts should be boxed," said the mate. This would give the bare masts extra support so the ice would not break them.

"A man'd freeze to death working on deck now," said a lieutenant. "Call the Old Man."

Glasgow went for the captain.

"Nobody can stay on deck long," the captain said, when they told him they wanted to box the masts. "We'll take turns on the bridge—and they'll be precious short turns, too. Mister Farragut, go bring some hot coals for the fire pots."

As Mister Farragut went to the galley after the hot coals, he could feel the ship moving. The wind was blowing it toward the rocky shore.

"Drop anchor!" the captain called. They dropped one anchor, then another. The wind dragged them both. They dropped a third—and a fourth. The wind grew stronger.

"We must cut the mast, or we'll be on the rocks by morning," Captain Porter decided.

The decks were smooth ice, and the masts were ice-coated. It was a windy ten degrees below zero—and it was Christmas.

"More shot in the fire pots!" the captain called.

Glasgow dumped lead shot on top of the live coals. The fire pots were like small stoves. They held the heat for a long while. However, they didn't hold enough heat for ten below zero.

The captain warmed his hands, then went back to the bridge. He ordered the mate to send some men forward with axes. Glasgow carried the axes. They chopped the mast away. As it fell and went overboard, the ship groaned and straightened a little.

"If this doesn't work, we'll spend our Christmas in Davy Jones' locker," the captain told them. Nobody wanted to do that, for Davy Jones' locker was at the bottom of the sea.

It worked—a Christmas miracle! As the masts were cut away, the icy wind dropped. The storm was ending, and the pink sun rose. The white snow turned into pink jewels.

"We'll get to the Christmas party after all," Mister Farragut said.

"Put on your uniform now, Farragut," said Mister Ogden. "I'll bet the buttons will fasten."

He was right. Mister Farragut had worked so hard that his vest buttoned easily.

They were gay on the way to the party. They thought they would be heroes when they told their story. They were wrong. Everyone there had been through the same danger. Some had suffered more than the men of the "Essex." No one cared about dancing. They were too tired. They had been through a danger that needed discussion with others who had been through it. The girls were pretty and sweet, but not one could save a ship from an ice storm. The ice storm was the real hero of that Christmas party.

This year Mister Farragut found the girls

tiresome. He danced for a while, but he grew tired. Finally he stretched out on a wide window sill and fell asleep. Mister Ogden had to shake him to get him awake in time to take his partner to supper.

"I could dance and sing all night, I'm so glad we're all alive," Mister Ogden said. He took his pretty partner's arm and led her toward the dance floor.

"I could sleep forever," said Mister Farragut, limping off in search of his supper partner. It was not long before he was as lively as ever. No one ever had a better time than Glasgow, when he finally got started.

"I told you the girls always like me!" he boasted to Mister Ogden.

Fire Drill

On June 20, 1812, Captain Porter called everyone on deck. Word had just come that the United States had declared war on Great Britain on June eighteenth. He read the Declaration of War aloud.

"I shall read this every day for three days," he said. "If anyone on the 'Essex' owes Great Britain allegiance and cannot pledge his loyalty to our country, I shall discharge him. In fact, I shall insist on his leaving this vessel."

No one came forward. The men on the "Essex" were loyal. They wanted to help win the war. They were glad that there was no longer a law to keep them from going to sea. They worked to get the "Essex" ready for war. Glasgow had never had so many duties.

The "Essex" had orders to join another squadron, off the coast of Brazil, in South America. If Captain Porter missed the squadron, he could go where he pleased. Glasgow hoped they would not find it. He knew that Captain Porter wanted to take the "Essex" around Cape Horn to the Pacific Ocean. Glasgow wanted to go there, too. He thought it would be exciting to make war on British whaling vessels, which were annoying American merchant ships.

Cape Horn was a long way from Norfolk, Virginia. They could not get there for a long while. There was much to be learned first.

There were daily gun drills now. Glasgow and the other midshipmen helped load the guns.

There were fire drills at any hour of the day or night. Glasgow's fire station was at the captain's boat, which he must be ready to lower into the water. In case of fire the captain and Glasgow would be the last ones to leave the "Essex."

Best of all Glasgow loved the sword practice. He was a better swordsman than many who were older and taller. He was light on his feet, quick and skillful. He would rather fence all day than study from books for an hour.

Besides all the extra drills there still were classes for the midshipmen. Glasgow was beginning to catch up with the other boys in reading and arithmetic. He liked books better now.

Midshipmen still ran to obey their officers. There were still those commands that sent Glasgow climbing the yards: "Away aloft, there!"

Once in a while he would see white sails against a blue sky. "Sail ho! Sail ho!" he would call down.

"Where away, Mister Farragut? Where away?" the officer of the day would call back.

104

"Three points off leeward, sir!" he would answer. Or "To the windward, sir!" His answer depended on whether the ship faced the wind, or was blown ahead by it.

Everyone was always watching for an enemy vessel. One day Mister Farragut looked out from aloft and saw a ship flying a British flag.

"Sail ho! Sail ho!" he called.

Quickly the "Essex" hoisted a British flag on her own mast, to make the enemy believe she was friend and not foe. This made it possible for the "Essex" to get near enough to the enemy to use her carronades. Her few long guns were not very much protection. As soon as she came close enough, down came the British flag and up went the Stars and Stripes. Glasgow felt deeply glad at sight of his own country's flag. He hated a British flag over the "Essex."

They captured the British ship, taking her by surprise. She carried fifty-five thousand dollars in gold. It was the richest prize they had found. The British officers were made prisoners of war and taken on board the "Essex." This made the "Essex" too crowded for comfort. Feeding these extra men cut down the "Essex" supplies, too.

The prisoners of war sat apart from their captors. They refused to admit they were prisoners. They were secretly planning a mutiny. Nobody on the "Essex" knew this, not even Mister Farragut, who spent most of his time watching the prisoners. The men would stop talking when he came near, or would change the subject. When he had gone on, they would return to their plans for taking over command of the "Essex."

"We'll make the captain turn the ship over to us," whispered their leader. "If he refuses, we'll kill him. Also, any officer of his who tries to help him will meet the same fate. By tomorrow the 'Essex' will join His Majesty's Navy."

That night, as Glasgow lay asleep in his hammock on the gun deck, something awakened him. He felt sure someone was standing over him in the darkness, though he could see no one. Yet he could feel someone watching him. Soon he was awake enough to know that it must be one of the British officers.

He lay very still, pretending to be asleep, but he kept one eye open. After a few minutes he could see that the watcher was the master of the enemy captain's gig, a young man but older than Glasgow. He was looking down at Glasgow, holding the boy's curved sword in his hand. Glasgow was too scared to move even an eyelash. This was lucky, for the young Britisher could not bring himself to murder a sleeping child. He moved on quietly.

Glasgow waited, not moving a muscle, hardly breathing. Soon the soft sound of the young Britisher's footsteps could no longer be heard. Glasgow caught his breath. He rolled from his hammock. It was as dark as pitch. He could not tell where the enemy officer lay in waiting. It was no time to think of danger, though. He must get to the Old Man's cabin!

He crawled on his stomach all the way to the quarter-deck. He opened and closed the captain's door without making a sound. Luck seemed to be with him! Now he must waken Captain Porter, without giving him a chance to cry out or make a sound. Glasgow knew that this would not be easy. The Old Man slept soundly. Glasgow put his hand over the captain's mouth, and then shook him by the shoulder. Now if he cried out, no one could hear him. Glasgow held the captain's lips tight together, telling him what had happened.

By that time Captain Porter was wide awake. "Stay here," he told Glasgow. "When you hear the bell, go to your station."

He left in the darkness. In a few minutes the

sound of the ship's big bell wakened everyone. It was followed by a sharp command.

"Fire! Fire! All hands to their stations!" came the command. Soon every bell on the "Essex" was ringing and every officer was shouting out orders.

"Fire! Fire! All hands to their stations!"

Glasgow ran through the darkness, repeating the words. He couldn't call very loud. He thought the British officers had set fire to the "Essex." Fire was the most terrible misfortune that could come to a sailing ship!

Yet Mister Farragut went straight to his station and waited for orders. Bells were clanging all over the ship now. Everyone was crying, "Fire! Fire!"

The men came running across the deck, wrapped in their blankets. Glasgow stood at his station, as he did in every fire drill. It was real this time, he thought. He lowered the cap-

110

tain's boat into the water, and wondered how long it would take to get the men off the burning ship.

The "Essex" officers went about doing what was expected of them. They did not seem frightened. It was the British officers who were frightened. They, too, believed that some of their own number had set fire to the "Essex." They pushed and shoved and crowded toward the small boats. They knew that prisoners would be the last to be saved.

Some of them jumped into the sea in their fright. Others prayed. "Save us, Lord, or we perish!" They were not religious men. They were terribly frightened. They did not know where to turn.

Captain Porter soon settled them. He ordered them put into irons and confined down in the hold for the rest of the voyage.

"There was no fire," said the captain. "It was

the best way I knew to get the mutineers up on deck. I knew the rest of you would behave just as you did behave. I am proud of you!"

The captain sent for Glasgow. "See that the cook gives the prisoners only three biscuits a day, and a half cup of fresh water flavored with lemon juice. We won't waste precious rations on men who would murder us."

Mister Farragut delivered the order to the mate, who told the bosun, who told the officer of the day, who carried the news to the galley, where the Chinese cook ruled.

The captain put his hand on Glasgow's shoulder. "Indeed, you saved our necks tonight, Mister Farragut."

Glasgow grinned as he saluted the captain. "Aye, sir," he admitted. Then he added, "You were a big help yourself, sir."

They both laughed.

112

Pigs and Horses

THE "ESSEX" approached Cape Horn early in February. She was still waiting for good weather three weeks later.

A sailing ship was at the mercy of the wind. It could lose in an hour what it traveled in a day. The weather was never good around Cape Horn, but it was better in summer than in winter. In Brazil and Chile and around the Cape, February was summer. That year the storms were as bad as though it were winter.

"All we can do is wait for a change in the weather," the captain told Mister Farragut. Three weeks later the captain had had to order half rations for everyone. Better half rations now than none at all later.

It was Midshipman Farragut's duty to hand out those half rations to the hungry, grumbling men. His own brown eyes had grown large with hunger, but he could not admit he was hungry, as the men could, and did. He could not even nibble at a single ship's biscuit that was not a part of his own rations. He was an officer, and must act like an officer.

He was also the pet of the whole ship. There was hardly a day when at least one old sailor did not offer him some of his own slim fare.

"I've been hungry before," one told him. "I'll be hungry again, more than likely. A little fellow like you, sir—you don't know how to go hungry. Here, take this biscuit. Drop this pinch of tea in this half cup of fresh water."

The boy set his lips before he could refuse. He could hardly keep from accepting.

"I'm not a child," he said angrily. "An officer can bear anything that his men can bear."

The captain, too, tried to force food on him. Mister Farragut would not take it.

"You don't have enough for yourself, sir." He refused the captain again and again.

The captain worried about him. He watched the boy grow thinner and thinner. His dark eyes seemed to grow larger and larger. His cheeks looked hollow and pale.

"Tomorrow we round the Horn," said the captain, finally. "Regardless of the weather."

Tomorrow, when it came, brought a storm with it. It was the worst storm of all. The wind stove in the ports from bow to quarter-deck. Water poured through the portholes. One of the small boats was lifted right off its davits, where it was fastened, blown overhead, and then dropped into the water by the wind.

Rain beat on them. It poured down the hatch-

115

ways that led to the steerage, the lowest deck.
The men down there thought that the ship was
sinking. The waves were as high as mountains,
it seemed to Glasgow. The sky was dark at noon.
The wind played with the "Essex" as though she
were a toy ship.

"Downes, help at the wheel," said the captain.
He sent two other lieutenants to help the sailing
master. Finally he and the first mate added their
strength to the others. It was a battle between
the men and the wind. It made Glasgow remember his father and the little boat in the storm on
Lake Pontchartrain. He thought of his father's
words, when the storm was over.

"Say your prayers! Get on your knees and
thank the good God for making our little boat
stronger than His great wind."

At last they made the ship obey the wheel, in
spite of the wind and the waves. The wind
roared and the waves roared, and the pumps

116

below deck made a whining sound, and then a sucking sound. The welcome sound of the pumps went on long after the wind and the waves had grown quiet.

Mister Farragut was too busy to have time to be frightened. Others were terribly frightened, though. The storm had made one side of the "Essex" look like a wreck.

Captain Porter ordered his men on deck. He told the bosun's mate, Mister Kingsbury, to talk to the men. Everyone liked Mister Kingsbury. He took one look at the frightened faces around him and roared, "Dad blast your eyes! We've got one whole side left, haven't we?"

Glasgow began to laugh. It made others laugh until soon everyone forgot to be frightened. If they could laugh together, they could work together to put the "Essex" in order.

The captain had the ship before the wind, letting the wind send them through the water.

Some of the men had gone after the small boat. They had brought it back safely and fastened it on its davits again. Carpenters began tearing away broken timbers and replacing them. Sailmakers took out their needles. Mister Farragut and the other midshipmen began to clean the deck of the splintered yards. There was enough kindling to last them for the rest of the voyage.

There was a wind again the next day. The "Essex" could no longer fight it. She had to go wherever the wind chose to blow her. Finally, from the rigging Mister Farragut called, "Land ho! Land ho!"

It was only a tiny island off the coast of Chile, but there would be food there. Too, one could feel good firm land beneath one's feet again. Some of the men repaired the ship. Others went ashore to hunt for horses and pigs. The pigs were really wild hogs, with horns on their heads. Glasgow watched the men drive the animals onto the ship. He thought the horses were beautiful. They were small, but well formed and lively. It seemed too bad to tie them in stalls. The hogs were not beautiful, though. Glasgow couldn't help laughing at them, they were so ugly.

"Looks like an Irishman, that one!" he said.

"Aye, that he does," agreed the Irish sailor who was helping load the animals. "Sure, he should have an Irish name, shouldn't he? We'll call him Murphy and make a nice pet of him. Shall we?"

Glasgow laughed at that.

The ship smelled of pigs now, but nobody minded. It meant there would be fresh meat at last, and no more half rations. There had been plenty of fruit on the island, too. Glory be, they would eat again!

They were around the Horn at last, and ready to hunt British whalers. They had to find out where to look for them. They stopped at port after port to get information. The captain would give the men shore leave.

"Go wherever you find sailors gossiping," he told them. "Mister Farragut, you understand Spanish. Go along and keep your ears open."

Mister Farragut listened hard. Back on the "Essex" he reported what he had learned about British whalers.

"Well done, Mister Farragut!" said the captain gratefully.

They began finding British whaling ships. The "Essex" took them prisoner. Whaling ships always carried plenty of food. No need for half rations on the "Essex" now!

Mister Farragut had his twelfth birthday. He was small and thin. A boy couldn't do much growing on half rations. He still liked to climb in the rigging and sit cross-legged on the yards, watching for whalers.

"Sail ho! Sail ho!" he called one day.

He called three times before the answer came. "Where away, Mister Farragut?"

It was a ship from Peru called the "Nereyda." Peru was on England's side in the war, and an enemy of the "Essex." They captured the "Nereyda" before she could get out her guns. Her captain admitted that he had two prize ships of his own with him, two American whalers. One of these was the "Alexander Barclay." The "Nereyda's" prizes were now Captain Porter's. The men on the "Barclay" cheered happily when they heard what had happened.

Captain Porter called his officers together and told them that he was going to send his three prize ships back to Valparaiso.

"The only trouble is, I don't have enough lieutenants left to send with them as commanders. We've already taken so many prizes."

The captain had heard good news the last time he'd been in Valparaiso. There had been a letter from Mrs. Porter telling him that a son had been born to them some months before. This news made him very happy.

The news didn't make David Glasgow Farragut happy, though. He was afraid the new baby, whose name was David Dixon Porter, would take his place with the captain.

"Three Davids in the same family are too many," he said unhappily. "Shall I give my name back to you?"

After that, the captain tried to find a way to make David Glasgow Farragut understand that he had not lost a father, but had gained a brother. Now, as Captain Porter thought about masters for the prize ships, he looked at Glasgow. He had a sudden idea.

"The prize master of the 'Alexander Barclay' will be—will be—Midshipman Farragut!" announced Captain Porter.

Someone started to laugh. Someone else

cheered, and after that all the others cheered, instead of laughing. The idea of putting a boy in command of a ship seemed to please them.

However, it didn't please the "Barclay's" glum old British captain from Liverpool, England. It didn't please him a bit.

"It's an insult to His Majesty's Navy!" he cried. "I'll not stand it!"

The Boy Commander

MISTER FARRAGUT was delighted when he heard that he was to be in command of the "Barclay." He rubbed his ear when the captain told him. He wasn't sure he had heard right. It was too much like a dream for him to believe it.

The glum old Liverpool captain was to be sailing master, but he was to take orders from Mister Farragut. A man of sixty, a man who had spent his whole life in His Majesty's Navy, was now to take orders from a twelve-year-old midshipman! No wonder the old fellow was disappointed and angry.

Quite a fleet was to go to Valparaiso—the

"Montezuma," the "Georgianna," the "Policy," the "Alexander Barclay." In charge of all was the "Essex Junior," which was the "Nereyda" renamed. Orders were for the "Essex Junior" to leave first and for the others to follow.

Mister Farragut stood on the bridge of the "Alexander Barclay," calling out orders to the American crew and the British sailing master.

"Fill the main-topsail!"

The British captain just glowered at him and did nothing whatsoever.

"I'm taking none of your orders, lad. You might as well know it. If you're not careful, you'll be finding yourself in Greenland before you know what has happened, too!"

"Not Greenland, sir. Valparaiso!" said Mister Farragut. "We'd better get started, too. Tell the men, sir, to fill the main-topsail."

The "Essex Junior" had pulled out of the harbor. The others were following—the "Montezuma," the "Policy." Only the "Alexander Barclay" was not in motion yet.

"Anchors aweigh! Fill the main-topsail!" he ordered, in his high, shrill voice.

IIe was not too young to recognize trouble. The British captain was not taking orders. He had plans of his own for the "Barclay." However, Mister Farragut had been ordered to take the "Barclay" in the wake of the "Essex Junior" to Valparaiso. It was his first command and he intended to see that it was successful.

"Fill the main-topsail! Close up with the 'Essex Junior'!" he ordered.

"Now you don't really mean it, lad, do you?" teased the captain. His broad face was still purple with anger. Suddenly he shook his big red fist in Glasgow's face. "You—you nutshell, you! Do you think I'd risk taking your orders?"

"Fill the main-topsails!" Glasgow repeated.

"I'll run my own course," said the British cap-

tain. "I give my own orders. Don't you be surprised if you see yourself off Labrador before
very long."

Mister Farragut filled his lungs with air and
yelled at the top of his thin voice, *"Fill the main-
topsail!"*

A man started toward the mainmast to obey.
The British captain roared at him. "Don't you
touch those ropes! Anyone who touches a rope
on this ship, except at my order, will be shot!"

The men murmured when they heard this.
Mister Farragut, however, had taken a quick
look at the captain's belt, and he had seen no
gun. That gave him the courage to ask the old
captain a question.

"What were you aiming to shoot *with*, sir?
You don't have a gun on your person!"

The captain looked confused and uncertain.
Then in his anger he left the helm and ran toward the quarter-deck.

128

"No, but I will have!" he yelled. "You'd better leave those ropes alone till I get back, if you want to go on living!"

Mister Farragut was uneasy. He knew he could never put down a mutiny, if one started. Still, the crew were Americans, weren't they? In spite of their training to respect authority, wouldn't they prefer an American midshipman commander to an English captain with an extremely bad temper?

He explained to a member of the crew that his orders were for the "Barclay" to follow the "Essex Junior." He told him the captain had refused to order the topsails filled.

The seaman saluted the twelve-year-old.

"Aye, aye, sir!" he said in a respectful tone.

Mister Farragut knew by the look in the man's blue eyes that he, and not the old captain, was recognized as the rightful commander of the "Barclay."

He took a deep breath of relief. He was among friends, after all! He knew his commands would be obeyed.

"Fill the main-topsail!" he ordered. The men ran to the ropes. The sails swelled. Glasgow himself took the wheel. They were soon out of the harbor, heading toward Valparaiso.

The new commander ordered the old captain confined to quarters until the "Barclay" caught up with the "Essex Junior." He sent a boy to the captain's cabin to tell him.

"If the captain dares show his face on deck without my permission, he will be shot!" said Mister Farragut. He knew that his loyal men would obey even this order if he were to ask it. He hoped he would not need to ask it.

He had no more trouble after that. It pleased the crew to see a pint-size midshipman giving commands to a captain. They had often wished to see just such an upset in the natural order.

130

"Farragut's full of fire, ain't he?" they said to one another. "We'll help him keep the old skipper in his place."

They laughed and sang at their work, as though life on board pleased them. One of their favorite chanteys was:

"Nancy Banana she married a barber!
   Haul her away, boys, haul her away!
   She married a barber who shaved with-
      out lather!
   Haul her away, boys, haul her away!"

They pulled at the heavy ropes in time to their chantey. A good song made their hard work seem a bit easier.

When they caught up with the "Essex Junior," Mister Farragut went aboard to report to Lieutenant Downes, his superior officer, what had happened on the "Barclay."

"I must hear the captain's side of it, too, Farragut," Lieutenant Downes told him, when Glasgow had finished his story.

The captain was in good spirits when he came on board the "Essex Junior." He showed no signs of anger at all.

"It was all just a joke, Lieutenant!" he insisted. "Why, I wouldn't have harmed a hair of the little fellow's head. I only wanted to scare him, so he'd turn the ship over to me. What can a lad his age know about sailing ships?"

"This one knows a good deal about sailing ships, Captain," said Lieutenant Downes.

Mister Farragut began to grow angry. "All just a joke, was it? Lieutenant Downes, ask him if I scared easily."

The British captain admitted good-naturedly that the boy had been stubborn. "He wouldn't give in at all." The captain looked thoughtful. Then he turned to Lieutenant Downes. "He's not likely to want to go the rest of the way with me as his sailing master, Lieutenant. Better just give me full command of the 'Barclay.' I promise to get her to Valparaiso."

"Oh, no!" cried Mister Farragut. "Captain Porter gave the command to me. You'll not take it away from me, will you, sir?"

The commander of the "Essex Junior" winked at the boy commander of the "Barclay." "Of course not," he said. Then he turned to the British captain. "Midshipman Farragut is in command of the 'Barclay,' sir, and you are its sailing master. If I hear of any more trouble, it will not be good for you, Captain. Need I remind you that you are still a prisoner of war?"

The captain knew when he was beaten. Smiling, he held out his hand and said, "Shall we be friends, Mister Farragut?"

Glasgow pretended that he did not see it. He looked at Lieutenant Downes. "I shall return to my ship, sir," said Mister Farragut. "Captain, you will follow me."

The glum captain was actually cheerful for the rest of the voyage. He sang songs and told stories. He made Mister Farragut think of old Captain Porter. Glasgow was almost fond of him by the time they arrived at Valparaiso.

"You're not the nutshell I thought you were," the old man confided. "The truth is, I was worse scared than you at first. I had no taste for trusting myself in these waters at this time of year with a nutshell who knew naught of sailing."

"I know a little," Mister Farragut said modestly. "I've had some fine teachers."

"I know now," said the captain.

"You've taught me a few things yourself. Did you know it?"

"I didn't intend to," the captain said. Then he grinned. "You're no nutshell," he said.

"I know," said Mister Farragut.

The "Essex" and the "Phoebe"

IN VALPARAISO, Glasgow again listened to sailors who spoke Spanish. In this city allied with Great Britain, Glasgow let no one know that he was an American. He was of Spanish blood, he told those who asked him about himself. His father was from Minorca. Men talked much more freely after they knew this. They, too, were of Spanish blood.

He learned many things. He learned that Captain Porter was worrying the British by the way he was capturing their whaling ships. He learned that Great Britain intended to stop it. He learned that British ships were even then on their way to find the "Essex" and recapture their whalers. They were sending one of their best ships, the "Phoebe," commanded by one of Britain's best Navy officers, Captain Hillyar.

The "Essex Junior" hurried back to tell Captain Porter all they had learned in Valparaiso. Captain Porter began getting his two ships ready to meet the "Phoebe." Hidden among the Galapagos Islands, they worked on the two ships, and when they were ready they went out to hunt for the "Phoebe."

It was Mister Glasgow on the "Essex" who finally found her.

The crew of the "Essex" was divided into three watches. One was on duty while the other two rested. Each watch worked four hours and then rested four hours.

One whole watch had gone ashore that afternoon. Glasgow, on duty, was aloft as usual. Suddenly he almost lost his balance.

"A sail! Sail ho!" he called down. Then, getting more and more excited, he added, "Two sails! Two sails!"

"Where away?" called the captain.

"Portward, sir," Glasgow called back. "Could it be the 'Phoebe,' sir?"

"It would be the time I'd pick, if I were the 'Phoebe's' commander," Captain Porter said.

Glasgow climbed down from the yards. "The captain of that British merchantman we saw in the harbor knows that a third of our men had shore leave. He must have got word to the 'Phoebe,' " he said.

"Light the signal, Mister Farragut," the captain ordered.

Glasgow lighted a red lantern and carried it aloft. He fastened it high on the mizzenmast. When the men saw it, it was a sign that meant: RETURN TO SHIP! ALL MEN TO THEIR STATIONS!

By the time the "Phoebe" began to move toward the "Essex" all the men were back and at their stations, waiting for battle.

Glasgow, standing on the bridge with the Old Man, could see Captain Hillyar standing on a long gun in the bow of the "Phoebe."

"What is he doing there?" Glasgow whispered to the captain.

"We must wait and see," said Captain Porter.

They waited a few moments.

"Captain Hillyar's regards to Captain Porter!" called the British captain. "Is Captain Porter well?"

"Quite well, sir!" Captain Porter called back. "*You* won't be well, if you come too near us!"

"Aye! That's right, sir!" called Glasgow, from sheer excitement.

"If I should happen to fall aboard your ship, of course it would just be an accident," mocked Captain Hillyar.

"You are too close now," Captain Porter answered. "If you touch a single rope yarn of this ship, I shall board your ship, sir!"

Glasgow nodded agreement, and turned to grin at the boarding party that stood close by. They were waiting for orders to board the "Phoebe" and fight the battle on her deck. Captain Porter blew on his trumpet, a signal for his men to drive off the "Phoebe."

The "Phoebe" was backing down, though. Her yards swept the bow of the "Essex" without touching a single rope. In his excitement Glasgow had climbed out on the bowsprit. The prow of the "Phoebe" was just above Glasgow's head. He reached his arm up to touch it. The captain shook his head. "No, Mister Farragut. Let her go. It isn't time."

Glasgow felt disappointed as he watched the "Phoebe" drop back and anchor half a mile behind. He sat in the stern of the "Essex" and watched the enemy until dark.

140

For two days the ships watched each other. The "Phoebe" was having supplies brought to her from Valparaiso. When she finally did move, she blockaded the entrance to the harbor. That kept the "Essex" and the "Essex Junior" bottled up where they were.

"We can't get into the harbor, or out to sea, either!" moaned Glasgow.

"We'll send out a boarding party tonight," Captain Porter said. "Maybe we can take her by surprise."

Glasgow had tied blankets around the oars, so that they couldn't be heard as the boarding party drew near the "Phoebe." He went along in the captain's boat, but he was too excited to be much help. He was shaking as though he'd been dipped in ice water. He wasn't afraid, though. He was just excited.

He was angry when the captain said, "Sh! Let's hear what the men on the 'Phoebe' are saying." They were close enough then to hear. The men on the "Phoebe" said they were ready and waiting.

"Turn around and go back to the 'Essex,'" ordered the captain. "Better luck next time." That command made Glasgow furious. He didn't want to go back to the "Essex." He wanted to board the "Phoebe."

There was more waiting. This was harder to bear, Glasgow discovered, than half rations. There were times when he thought he could stand it no longer. Waiting on an enemy seemed so senseless.

One morning Captain Porter said to Glasgow, "Keep aloft as much as you can today. I've sent a message to Captain Hillyar. I told him that if he will send his companion ship, the 'Cherub,' to the farthest part of the harbor, I will come out and fight him."

"Was the 'Cherub' the second sail I saw?"

"Aye. Keep your eyes on her now!"

All day Glasgow watched the enemy. In mid-afternoon he saw a new flag on the "Phoebe." It was the answer to Captain Porter's own battle flag that said FREE TRADE AND SAILORS' RIGHTS. The new flag on the "Phoebe" said GOD AND OUR COUNTRY—BRITISH SAILORS' BEST RIGHTS. Did that mean they were getting ready to fight soon? He heard a gun fired to windward. What would that mean? Slowly the "Cherub" started to sail around the "Phoebe" to leeward.

Glasgow was screaming without making sense now, he was so excited. He slid down the ropes so quickly that his right hand was burned and bleeding.

"This is it! This is it!" he cried hoarsely.

The captain blew his trumpet. Glasgow knew what that meant. CLEAR FOR ACTION! ANCHOR AWEIGH!

Glasgow couldn't stand still now. He was

143

darting around the deck like a goldfish. The squeak of the windlass as it pulled up the anchor sounded as loud as a cannon.

Then, before the "Essex" had more than started toward her enemy, the "Phoebe" lifted her studding and hurried out to sea. She reminded Glasgow of a lady lifting her skirts to run. He was disgusted. Once again, there would be no battle! There would be more waiting. Already this was the middle of March, 1813.

On the twentieth there was a storm from the south. It dragged the anchors on the "Essex" and she drifted out to sea with a broken cable. Her main-topmast had been broken off by the wind, too, but it was her broken cable that kept her from getting back into the harbor.

"Can't something be done?" Mister Farragut fumed. "Suppose the 'Phoebe' should come out and fight us now?"

"Hillyar is not the man to miss such a fine opportunity," Captain Porter said. "It couldn't be better for them or worse for us. We must do our best, anyway."

Captain Porter looked grim. Glasgow could see that no one on board thought they had a chance for success. It upset him to see everyone so discouraged. They were expecting defeat before going to battle.

"We could at least hope for victory," he said. "Surely something will happen to save us."

It wouldn't have been so bad if the "Essex" had had long enough guns, or if they could have fixed the cable. The captain tried to put a spring on the cable, but the spring broke.

At four o'clock the watch changed and Glasgow came on duty. He had served with the other watches all day, but this was his own watch.

"Away aloft!" the captain ordered.

Glasgow groaned. For once he would have preferred to stay below. He wanted company.

However, from the rigging he could see as well as hear the "Phoebe" fire the first shell from her long guns. She was under the stern of the "Essex," too far away for the carronades to reach her. The "Cherub" was nearer, on the starboard bow, so the "Essex" opened fire on the "Cherub." Glasgow chuckled when he saw the "Cherub" hurry to hide behind her big sister, the "Phoebe."

He went down on deck to report the "Cherub's" position. "We've got her on the run! We're too hot for her!" he boasted.

Then the "Phoebe" let go with her long guns. There was a sound of splintered wood, and men crying out in pain. A sailor who had once offered Glasgow his rations fell down on the deck, his hand clutching his wounded shoulder.

Glasgow felt sick at his stomach. He was so dizzy that he could see nothing clearly. Everything went round and round. The rest of the day was a bad dream. All he knew was that men

146

yelled at him to go here, do this, wait there, find this one or that one. He ran from duty to duty, not conscious of what he was doing. He dodged splinters and put out fires and loaded guns. He was everywhere at once, and not really anywhere. He worked in a nightmare.

Once he heard Captain Porter cry, "This is not battle. It is murder. They give us no chance to defend ourselves."

He heard men talk about a cable spring that kept breaking and a sail that wouldn't fill so that they could get into the harbor. As he stumbled across the deck on some errand or other, he saw the door of a cupboard half open. A piece of sail hung through the opening. He tugged at the sail and dragged it across the blood-spattered deck to the captain.

"Look, sir. A jib. Would it do?"

The captain looked at it. "Where did you find it, Glasgow?"

"I don't know," Glasgow said. That quickly he had forgotten. He went along to watch the men break out the jib and tighten it in place. He looked at the sea and hated it for being so quiet. How could it be quiet in all this terror and fire and death?

When the sail was in place, he prayed for wind. "Fill the jib, please. Fill the jib!" He didn't know he was crying, but his face was wet.

His prayer was answered. The jib filled! Now there was some chance for the "Essex" to get beyond the reach of the "Phoebe's" long guns! The "Phoebe" moved nearer, though, and shot the spring off the cable.

The captain himself was crying now. "Gather my officers, Mister Glasgow. We must burn the 'Essex.'"

There weren't many officers left by that time.

"I plan to head for shore and set fire to the ship. I want your permission to do so."

149

Sorrowfully they agreed to this. All but Mister Farragut.

"No! No! No, no, no!" Mister Farragut objected violently. Why, it was like setting fire to his own home!

"Sorry, fellow! You're overruled," said the captain softly. "Let's take a look at the powder magazine, Mister Farragut. Do you think we have enough powder to blow up the 'Essex'?"

The "Phoebe's" guns kept on firing. The "Essex" was sinking now. The captain again sent for his officers. Lieutenant McKnight was the only one able to get there.

"We'll have to surrender," the captain said.

"Aye," agreed the lieutenant.

"No! No!" Mister Farragut sobbed. "There is enough powder to burn her."

"Enough powder, but not enough time," Captain Porter said.

The ship's clock was striking five bells. The

captain and his lieutenant looked at each other. The captain paced the deck. Mister Farragut walked behind him, his hands in his pockets, like the captain. Without turning around, the captain said, "The white flag. We surrender."

Mister Farragut went to call out the order. His voice broke.

"The white flag!" he called, but he could not say that worst of all words, *surrender!*

Murphy the Pig

THE "Phoebe" sent a boarding party to the "Essex" for Captain Porter's surrender. Glasgow could not look at them. He felt cold all over, as though he were coming down with a sickness.

He hurried down to the sick bay, to get away from the British. He couldn't bear the sick bay, either. Still, these wounded and dying men were his friends and he loved them. As he stood watching the doctor, the dream ended. He was not walking through a nightmare now. This was real. This was war, and it was horrible. He sank down on the deck and buried his face in his elbow and cried like a baby.

The surgeon found him crouching there and joggled his elbow.

"What's this!" said the surgeon. "A whole healthy young body. Come on now! Get to work. Don't waste time this way!"

Mister Farragut found himself bathing wounds with hands that trembled. Hands were important. It took both of Glasgow's to hold the rough hand of one seaman while the doctors cut off his leg, but he didn't let go for a minute.

He was bringing fresh water to the wounded when Captain Porter came for him.

"So you're busy," the captain said. Glasgow thought he looked old and tired and as though he, too, had been crying. "They must need you badly. When you have finished, join me on board the 'Phoebe.' We are prisoners, but I've asked permission to have you stay with me."

Mister Farragut wanted to say that he'd rather die than set foot on the "Phoebe." He didn't, though. Soon the surgeon came to him. He had to talk loudly to be heard above the noise of the pumps and the moans of the wounded.

"You'd better go, Mister Farragut. The others are going—all who can stand on their own legs."

Mister Farragut followed the others sadly.

He stood alone, down in the steerage of the "Phoebe." He felt a deep, choking sorrow within him, but he was no longer crying.

The steerage was crowded. Now and then he could pick out an "Essex" man by his voice. The familiar voice sounded good. Suddenly he hated British voices—especially when they were laughing! Just behind him he could hear a young British voice, chuckling.

Glasgow turned to look.

"See the fine prize I've got!" The British boy laughed. "A lovely fat grunter! A beautiful juicy porker! He's all mine, too, because I found him first."

Mister Farragut gasped. He was furious. "He's not yours!" he cried out. "He's my property. He's my pet pig! He's Murphy!"

This was half true. Murphy belonged to the "Essex," but not to any one person. He was the ship's mascot. Now Glasgow really believed the pig had been his forever. No Britisher should have him. No-sirree!

"Yours, you say?" teased the British boy. "Why, you belong to us yourself, prisoner! So does the grunter. Only he belongs to *me* because I found him!"

Murphy had managed to wriggle out of the British boy's arms. He ran crazily around the deck, squealing as though he were being butchered. Finally he hid behind the ropes and chests that were being brought from the "Essex."

The men were laughing. Mister Farragut wasn't, though. He wanted Murphy and he intended to have him at any cost.

"Even a Britisher can't take away a man's private property!" cried Mister Farragut. "Among honorable men the world over—though you wouldn't know about honorable men—a prisoner of war is allowed to keep his own property. Murphy is mine and I mean to have him! Just try to keep me from taking him!"

Mister Farragut started toward the chests behind which Murphy was catching his breath. The men held him back.

"Wait!" they cried. "The two of you fight for the porker. He'll belong to whichever one is the winner!"

The Britisher, who was older and taller, chose swords. This pleased Mister Farragut immensely. He was used to fencing with boys older and taller than he was.

He started awkwardly, which made the Britisher careless. It was easy to catch him off guard then. A quick lunge and a graceful turn of the

157

sword, and the British boy's sword fell clattering to the deck.

The men from the "Essex" cheered as though they had indeed won a battle.

"The li'l Yank's real good, hain't 'e?" called out a British voice. " 'E 'andles 'is sword like a gentleman, almost!"

Mister Farragut hugged the grunting pig, his cheek against Murphy's smelly hide. The pig stuck his nose into Glasgow's pocket. The warm, strong smell of him made Glasgow feel good. This was one thing from the "Essex" that the "Phoebe" had not taken!

Someone called his name. He held the pig closer. A British midshipman came to him. "Your name Farragut?"

"Aye, sir," answered Glasgow. Then he was sorry for the "sir."

"Captain Hillyar will see you in his cabin. Most irregular, if you ask me."

Glasgow hadn't asked him anything—then.

"Do I have to go there? I'm not under your Captain Hillyar."

"Captain Porter is with Captain Hillyar. Don't you Yanks obey your own captain?"

"Is it all right to bring Murphy?"

"A pig in the captain's cabin?" The midshipman was horrified. "That may be all right on the 'Essex,' but not here!"

An "Essex" man whispered to Glasgow, "I'll take care of Murphy. Don't you worry, sir!"

Glasgow went with the midshipman.

Captain Porter was eating breakfast in Captain Hillyar's cabin. Glasgow felt sick when he saw him there.

"Captain Porter wants you to have breakfast," said Captain Hillyar kindly.

Glasgow hadn't forgotten all that had happened. "There was no time to eat," he said. "I worked with the wounded."

"There's time now," said the captain. "What would you like?"

"I have no appetite for your food, sir!" cried Mister Farragut.

Captain Porter set down his cup of tea and called out, "Mister Farragut! I expect you to keep a civil tongue in your head! Captain Hillyar has been good enough to offer you breakfast. A cup of hot tea will help get the kinks out of your stomach. Sit down here beside me and thank the captain."

"It will get no kinks out of my stomach, sir, if I have to eat in the same room with Captain Hillyar!"

Captain Porter looked angry. He turned to Captain Hillyar, as though asking for his understanding. "The boy's had a rough time this morning," he said. "This is his first taste of battle. Surely you can remember how it was with yourself."

160

Captain Hillyar nodded. "We all remember—too long. We go to sea too young, Captain Porter. All of us." He poured out a cup of steaming hot tea and set it down before Mister Farragut.

"No good taking it so hard, boy. It's the fortunes of war, you know. Next time it may be your turn to win."

The Hard Decision

DAVID GLASGOW Farragut did not know that fifty years would pass before he had his victory. He had been an able naval officer ever since he was twenty. Now that he was sixty he knew that even victories could be bitter.

Early in 1861 Captain Farragut and his second wife, Virginia Loyall, and their son Loyall came home to Norfolk, Virginia, from California, where Captain Farragut had finished building a United States Navy Yard on Mare Island. It was built like the navy yard in Norfolk. The captain hoped he would now be given a squadron to command, for he felt that he had earned it.

The Farraguts soon realized that America had changed while they were in California. The North and the South had grown apart. Now they were very close to war.

The South thought the federal government was denying them their rights as free states. They believed money collected at Southern ports should belong to the state in which it was collected. They claimed, too, that any state might leave the Union when she felt her rights had been abused. They had many reasons for feeling resentful.

Even some Northerners believed that the Southern States should be allowed to leave the Union if they were not satisfied. South Carolina had already left. Other states planned to follow her and form a new union called the Confederate States of America.

Virginia had voted to stay with the Union. This was good news to the Farragut family, whose home was in Norfolk, Virginia. Sometimes it seemed to them that half the state was related to Virginia Farragut. They did not want to be separated from their relations and friends.

Then came what the South called an invasion by federal forces at Charleston, South Carolina, and the firing on Fort Sumter, and the President's Declaration of War. Virginia changed her mind quickly and joined the Confederacy.

Norfolk promptly began recruiting a Confederate navy. If the same thing that had happened at Charleston should happen in Norfolk, they would need to defend themselves. If the forts belonged to the states in which they were situated, so did the navy yard. Was it not built on Virginia soil?

The authorities in Washington did not agree with all this. The government said that a country's defenses belonged to the government and not to any state alone. It was the duty of any

President to protect and preserve his country's property.

Indignant Southern navy officers were resigning to join the Confederate navy. Captain Farragut was offered command of a squadron if he would join the navy. He refused.

"When I was eight years old, I took a vow to protect the United States of America. I have no reason to break that vow now," he said.

"Then you must get out of Norfolk, or we will have to make you a prisoner of war," they answered him.

"Mind what I tell you," he warned them. "You fellows will be in trouble before you're through with this business."

Yet he knew that he would have to leave Norfolk. Sadly he told Virginia his plans.

"I must leave here tonight," he said. "Alone. I cannot take you and our boy away from your family. I cannot ask you to live among total strangers up North, while I fight a war against our own people."

Virginia smiled at him. "I knew this was coming," she told him. "I have been packing for days. How soon must we go?"

They left Norfolk the night the navy yard was in flames, set by Union officers to keep it from enemy hands. They went to Kingston, New York, which was about as far north as they could go and still be in their own country. The Captain waited impatiently, expecting his orders any day. However, the United States Navy was not handing out high commands to Southern officers without the most careful screening.

The Captain's dark, Spanish complexion and his wife's soft Southern accent started gossip in Kingston. Some said they must be freed slaves, or else runaways. Other people were sure they were spies, sent north to find out what was going on along the Hudson River. The Farraguts were delightfully friendly people, but they made no friends in Kingston.

When the Captain's orders came, he was given a desk job instead of a squadron. He could see nothing good in such a job, except that it took him and his family to New York, away from the petty cruelties of Kingston.

Late in November they had a most welcome caller—Captain David Porter, son of the Captain Porter who had been Glasgow's foster father. Captain Porter was building a mortar flotilla and his duties kept him busy shuttling between New York and Washington. He could not have found the time for such a visit if President Lincoln and Secretary of the Navy Gideon Welles had not sent him there on a mission.

After the first joy of meeting and their eager questions about families and friends, Captain Porter said, "Glasgow, I've come on business. First, I must pledge you to strict secrecy."

"You should know me well enough not to need such a pledge, Dave," Glasgow told him.

"There is a plan to start an offensive expedition up the Mississippi River this spring," explained Porter. "Our blockades are not perfect. Supplies reach New Orleans from Texas by way of the Red River. If we could take New Orleans and control the Mississippi, we could split the Confederacy in two."

"It is the thing to do, Dave. I've thought so for weeks," agreed Farragut.

"The plan is for a joint undertaking, with army and navy supporting each other. The President is trying to find a loyal and able officer to carry the plan through and he would like to find one who knows the Mississippi River. Most of our navy know more about Japanese waters and West Africa than about their own rivers. Glasgow, does this interest you at all? I was sent here purposely to ask you."

"Does it interest me?" Farragut repeated with a grin. "You know how inactivity bores me. Will I finally be a flag officer with a squadron?" It had been a long time since he had felt so good.

"I don't know. I can't promise, of course, but I don't see how it could be anything else. I told them that I had learned from you all I know of the river, and I suggested they might talk to you. Since then the Navy has been asking questions. They like your loyalty."

Farragut was still for a while. Then he said, "My father and yours and the river—that was my boyhood, what I had of it, Dave. Strange that it should suddenly seem of great value."

"They want you in Washington just as soon as possible, Glasgow. Could you leave early in the morning?"

A pleasant dinner in the home of Secretary Welles easily won for Captain Farragut his new duty—that of flag officer of the newly formed

Western Gulf Blockading Squadron. Few knew why it had been created, and even fewer knew what its objectives were.

Yet, Gideon Welles, in his orders to his new flag officer, had written that "The most important operation of the war is confided to you and your brave associates. If successful, you will open the way to the sea for the great West, never again to be closed, and the flag to which you have been so faithful will fly again in every state."

Captain Farragut's new squadron was made up of old sailing sloops too heavy for shallow water, some steam frigates and new and untried gunboats, and a side-wheeler, the "Mississippi," from Commodore Perry's Japanese squadron. The mortar flotilla, the ironclads, were made over from whaling vessels and ferryboats. New ships were not yet completed.

Captain Farragut divided his fleet into three

parts—Red, Blue, and Red and Blue. His flagship, the "Hartford," led the Blue division. He had wanted to lead the parade, but his officers would not agree to this. His men and officers loved him, and they finally made him see that if anything happened to him, the whole undertaking would be threatened.

New Orleans was protected by two forts, Fort St. Philip and Fort Jackson. The Red division would engage Fort St. Philip, while the Blue would keep its guns on Fort Jackson. The third division, the light gunboats, would go upstream toward New Orleans, with the other divisions protecting them.

The Confederates were also brave and daring. Their River Defense Fleet went into action, while the forts fired on the Gulf fleet. The Confederate ram, the "Manassas," headed toward the "Mississippi," whose pilot was a young lieutenant named George Dewey. With unbelievable skill, Dewey turned his ship to face the "Manassas" and ran her to cover.

The Confederates had fastened a heavy cable under the water, from one side of the river to the other. They had piled wreckage beneath it, to keep ships from advancing. Farragut's men cut the cable and cleared a way for the ships. Fireboats drifted over the water and the ships had to avoid them or have their own ships fight fire. One of the ships got out of line and ran into the uncut end of the cable. The "Hartford," as it went by, sent boats to pick up the shipwrecked.

The forts were finally silenced. The Stars and Stripes waved gaily from New Orleans public buildings. Farragut had guessed it would take forty-eight hours to take New Orleans. It took six days and nights. The Confederates were very brave.

General Butler, United States Army, set up a

military government in New Orleans. He fed those who were hungry and gave medicine to the sick. Farragut, too, made the city his headquarters. The people soon learned that the Union men were not so bad as they had been painted.

Captain Farragut went to visit his sister, who lived in New Orleans. He wanted to see if there was anything she might need that he could give her. When she came to the door, she would not let him in the house. She called him names—"Traitor! Murderer! Starver of little children!"

Farragut was deeply hurt. He had not seen his sister for years. She was the only one of his father's family still alive. Yet she called him names when he was defending his country, when he was preserving the Union he had vowed to protect.

Though New Orleans was now a Union city, still the Confederacy was not yet split in two. It was only the first step toward the war's end.

Captain Porter and Captain Farragut both thought that they should hurry on to Mobile, while Mobile was still shocked over the fall of New Orleans and before she had time to build new defenses. However, President Lincoln ordered Captain Farragut to go up the river and take Vicksburg. This meant that he must take his ocean-going vessels three hundred miles inland, through water much too shallow for most of his fleet. If the river should fall, as it very often did in the winter, his fleet would be trapped in enemy country.

Farragut took his crippled ships and a thousand soldiers—rumor said that there were eight thousand rebel soldiers in Vicksburg—and found that his battle this time was more with the river than with the enemy. Ships ran into each other, got stuck on sandbars, lost their anchors, broke their timbers.

A messenger was sent to Vicksburg, demanding the city's surrender. Vicksburg sent back this message—"Mississippians don't know and refuse to learn how to surrender to an enemy. If Commodore Farragut or Brigadier General Butler can teach them, let them try."

The upper and lower Mississippi were now in the hands of the Union. However, from Vicksburg to Baton Rouge, it was still Confederate. In order to have free use of the entire river, it was necessary to take Vicksburg.

Shortage of coal, shortage of river pilots, shortage of ships and of troops to hold the city after it had once been taken, made any chance for success seem unlikely. Mosquitoes and malaria made it even worse.

None of Farragut's officers wanted to undertake a siege of Vicksburg in those conditions. One officer even said that if anyone was fool enough to try it, they could have his ship. Farragut promptly removed him from the responsibility of deciding. After weighing all sides, while he himself was ill with arthritis, he then decided to take his broken ships and his sick men back to New Orleans while there was still enough water in the river to float them.

Vicksburg's blockade had been weakened, but she had not surrendered.

The Confederate news report, which was the only news the President could get from the Lower Gulf, said that Farragut had been repulsed. This would mean the mission had failed. The messages that finally reached Captain Farragut in New Orleans were not full of praise.

Captain Farragut tried to explain to the navy. "The elements of destruction in that river are beyond anything I ever met. If the same destruction continues, the whole navy will be gone in twelve months. More anchors have been lost and vessels ruined than I have seen in a lifetime. Vessels which do not run into others are themselves rammed and crushed. I have not at the moment one-third of the needed vessels fit for duty outside. If struck by the ram 'Arkansas,' which they say is near Vicksburg, not one can resist her."

In March he once again took his ships up the river. He took Port Hudson, blockaded the Red

River, lost the "Mississippi," and joined Captain Davis' Western Flotilla. He tried to get Captain Davis to move his light ships up the river, while his own squadron would protect them, but Captain Davis thought this was too dangerous. Finally Secretary Welles ordered him back to New Orleans. Never had he obeyed orders more willingly. His ships needed mending and he and his men were sick with malaria.

In April he tried again. This time it was different. Captain Porter would meet him below Vicksburg, and his old friend, General Sherman, would be waiting with troops above the city. Even then it took several weeks. Vicksburg was still brave. Her courageous people had to be starved into surrender.

On the third day of July, Confederate General Pemberton asked for an armistice. On the Fourth, the city surrendered. It was a sad Independence Day for the people of Vicksburg, but a triumphant one for the Western Gulf Blockading Squadron. They were sure now that the war would soon be over.

After the fall of Vicksburg, Captain Farragut once again obeyed orders—he went home on leave. It was a leave he was needing badly. When he came back to New Orleans, his wife and his son were with him. Even war would be less dreadful with them beside him.

Admiral Farragut

THE NEW year, 1864, brought Farragut an unexpected promotion. In the old navy, captain was the highest rank. Commodore was more a title of honor than of rank. A commodore was still a captain. New offices had been created, and the boy who had long ago signed into the navy as midshipman had now become its first admiral. His whole life had been one of loyal, able, intelligent service to the United States Navy.

His service was not ended with promotion, either. The Mississippi River could not flow peacefully until Mobile belonged to the nation. Farragut was impatient to start his new duty. It meant that he would face his old friend, Franklin Buchanan, commander of the Confederate Navy. Farragut and "Old Buck" had served together in the navy since childhood. Now each thought the other a traitor. They might have to fight it out to prove which one was right.

Farragut learned that the new Confederate ram, the "Tennessee," would soon be ready for action. From Southern news reports, it was to be the last word in fast, low-draught ships. If he could move on Mobile before the "Tennessee" had her guns in place, if he could surprise Old Buck without the help of his new wonder ship, the rest would be easy.

There were delays and more delays. The iron flotilla that was being built for his use proved so heavy with gadgets, thought up by bright young engineers, that the ships all but sank under their own weight when tested. It was a great disappointment.

At least the useless waiting had given him time to make and unmake and remake his battle plans. If he could get his hands on even two more ironclads, he believed he could do the work he had waited so long to do.

His last ironclad, the "Tecumseh," had stopped so long for repairs that she arrived only a few hours before he gave the word to go.

It was Friday. Every sailor knew that Fridays were unlucky. It was raining, too, which was just as unlucky as Friday. The two taken together were really bad. The men shook their heads, but they obeyed orders anyway.

On the "Hartford" the admiral ate breakfast with Captain Drayton, his flag officer.

"At least, the wind's from the southwest," said the admiral. "One thing in our favor!"

Drayton nodded. "The smoke from our guns will blow straight into Fort Morgan." He raised his head for a glance at the fort's tower. Then he smiled. "Admiral, look! The sun!" he cried. "The sun is out!"

"The men will be glad," the admiral said.

Three forts guarded Mobile Bay—Fort Morgan, Fort Powell, and Fort Gaines. They were strong forts. A line of torpedoes had been strung under the water, almost all the way from Fort Morgan to Fort Gaines. Ships passing over them would explode them. Admiral Farragut was glad he knew about them in time. A red buoy that bobbed innocently on the water marked the end of the string. Within that red buoy lay death. Outside it there was a good chance for success. Farragut explained this to his officers.

Torpedoes were not the only dangers. North of Fort Morgan lay the ironclad ram, the "Tennessee," the Confederate wonder ship. It had been waiting in the Gulf for three months, hoping for a chance to break Farragut's blockade and open an attack on the Gulf Squadron. The

"Tennessee's" commander was the brave Franklin Buchanan. Old Buck had commanded rams before—the "Merrimac," the "Arkansas," and now the "Tennessee."

The admiral drained his third cup of tea. "We might as well start," he said quietly.

Captain Drayton rose quickly. "As my old French master used to say at examination time, 'Vee hopes vee vill do as vell as vee hopes vee vill do.'" Then he left to give the order that would start the fleet up the bay, past the forts and the "Tennessee."

By the time the admiral followed, the sky was clear. Was their luck turning?

Admiral Farragut had planned for his ships to move in a double column, each with a monitor lashed to her side. If either became disabled, the other could tow her to safety. The monitor would also be a protection to the side of the wooden ship that faced the fort.

184

Again Farragut had wanted to lead the way. Again his officers had protested. The "Brooklyn," they said, had a device on her that could sweep aside any torpedoes as she went over them. The "Brooklyn," with its monitor, the "Octorara," went first. Then came the "Hartford," with the "Metacomet," the "Richmond," with the "Port Royal," the "Lackawanna," with the "Seminole," the "Monongahela," with the "Kennebec." The monitors "Tecumseh," "Manhattan," "Winnebago," and "Chickasaw" flanked the procession, looking like the floating "cheese boxes" they had been nicknamed.

The admiral took his favorite place in the port rigging. As the battle went on, he climbed higher and higher until one of his officers remembered he had once suffered a dizzy spell.

The officer was worried. "Go tie the Old Man in the rigging," he told his aide.

Farragut smiled at the youngster as he felt

the cable about his waist. He knew he could still hold on, but the little attention pleased him. Even in battle, his men thought of his safety.

They heard the "Tecumseh" fire on Fort Morgan, and they heard the fort answer. The "Hartford" held her fire, but when the order did come, she fired as truly as though she were hitting a target. The hit won the attention of every enemy gunboat. The whole Confederate fleet was aiming at the "Hartford." Her mainmast was shattered. Splinters were falling thicker than snowflakes. On wooden ships, splinters caused far more casualties than did enemy guns.

At ten-thirty, the "Tecumseh" was opposite Fort Morgan, ready to pass the "Tennessee." Suddenly she paused, reeled, and sank out of sight. Her crew went down with her.

The "Brooklyn" began to back, crowding the ships behind her.

"What's wrong with the 'Brooklyn'?" called

out the admiral. "She should have plenty of water there."

"Aye, and to spare, sir," answered the "Hartford's" pilot, who had seen what happened.

By that time the admiral also knew what had happened. The "Tecumseh" had gone too close to the red buoy. Just a few inches clear of the buoy and she would have gone through safely. The fleet's guns seemed to have stopped firing, even the "Hartford's."

"What's the trouble?" Admiral Farragut called to the "Brooklyn" through his trumpet.

"Torpedoes!" called back Captain Alden.

Admiral Farragut knew that delay would be fatal to all of them.

"Pass the 'Brooklyn' and take the lead," he ordered his flag captain. Then to Captain Alden he trumpeted, "Follow me!"

The "Hartford" went around the "Brooklyn" and took the lead. The other ships followed.

They were on their way up the bay and would soon reach harbor.

Boats were sent for the survivors of the "Tecumseh." Why hadn't they obeyed orders?

Later, when Captain Buchanan, of the "Tennessee," saw the admiral's flagship a mile ahead of his fleet, with the other ships too busy firing on the forts to give their flagship much protection, he started after it.

He seemed to be aiming straight at the "Hartford," as though to ram her. This the "Hartford" had been expecting, and they were prepared for it. However, the "Tennessee" turned suddenly and began firing broadside. This the "Hartford" was not expecting, and was not, at that moment, prepared for. The other ships saw it and hurried to help her.

Not one of them could make even a dent in the "Tennessee's" iron sides. She seemed to be a charmed ship, one not to be conquered.

188

Admiral Farragut decided that he would go after the "Tennessee" himself, when dusk made it impossible for the lookouts at the forts to tell which ship belonged to which navy. He would use the monitor "Manhattan," and it would be like the old days when he was a young man chasing pirate ships.

Captain Buchanan, however, did not intend to wait until darkness. The "Tennessee" went speeding after first one Union ship and then another. She used the same tactics she had used on the "Hartford." She would go toward a ship as though meaning to ram her, then turn so quickly that the enemy could not prepare for her gunfire. Farragut's own guns did not hurt her. It seemed truly uncanny.

"Gunboats go after enemy gunboats!" ordered Farragut, handing a knife to the commander of the "Metacomet," which was lashed to the "Hartford." The sailors cut the connecting cable.

The "Manhattan's" commander knew of Farragut's plan to use his ship. He had listened to Farragut's estimate of the "Tennessee." Farragut had thought the "Tennessee" was a charm ship. He now saw her weak spot. Her steering gear was exposed. An enemy could get to it without much trouble. The "Manhattan" decided to try for the steering gear.

The admiral's plan worked. The charmed ship was soon crippled. Her brave commander had been almost fatally wounded.

As Admiral Farragut watched the white flag raised on the "Tennessee," he thought of the "Essex." He knew how Old Buck was feeling. Nothing was so hard to bear as surrender. He had never dreamed that when his long-expected victory would finally come, his old friend Buchanan would be the conquered one. At least he would see that Old Buck had the best doctors, and that everything possible would be done for his comfort. Maybe he could make a Union man of Old Buck yet!

The war had to end soon. Without the Mississippi River, the South could not hold out long. Surrender would be better than starving.

Mobile was as stubborn as Vicksburg had been. She refused to change flags until after General Lee had surrendered to General Grant.

It was spring before the war actually ended. How much longer it would have lasted, how many more brave young lives would have been taken, if there had been no Western Gulf Blockading Squadron, no one could say. It might have gone on for years.

As soon as Richmond, Virginia, was open, the Farragut family went there. It was good that Virginia was not enemy soil. However, Farragut felt that he could no longer live in the South. Too many of his friends still thought him a traitor. To America, though, he was a hero.

When Admiral Farragut was asked to run for the Presidency, he answered, "The one thing I know is the navy. When I was a red-headed midshipman, I promised to serve with all my ability in the navy. I've always done that, and I think I'd better stick to my promise."

During his long tour as commander of the European Squadron in 1867, he received many honors at all his ports of call. In the summer of 1869 he visited Mare Island in California, where he had long ago established a navy yard.

The Admiral was always interested, active, and busy—even to the time of his death, in 1870, at Portsmouth, New Hampshire.

A colossal bronze statue of Admiral Farragut was erected in Washington, D.C., by the United States Government. A similar one, erected on Madison Square in New York, also does honor to one of the most famous men in United States naval history.

More About This Book

WHEN DAVID FARRAGUT LIVED

1801   JAMES GLASGOW FARRAGUT WAS BORN AT CAMPBELL'S STATION, TENNESSEE, JULY 5.

There were sixteen states in the Union.

Thomas Jefferson was President.

The population of the country was approximately 5,500,000.

1807   THE FARRAGUT FAMILY MOVED TO NEW ORLEANS.

The Embargo Act, prohibiting exports to Great Britain and France was passed, 1807.

Robert Fulton built the "Clermont," the first practical steamboat, 1807.

Anthracite coal was burned for the first time in an open grate, 1808.

1810   GLASGOW WAS APPOINTED A MIDSHIPMAN AND WAS RENAMED DAVID GLASGOW FARRAGUT.

The War of 1812 was fought, 1812-1815.

"The Star-Spangled Banner" was written, 1814.

Florida was purchased from Spain, 1819.

The first steamship crossed the Atlantic, 1819.

The Erie Canal was completed, 1825.

The Mexican War was fought, 1846-1848.

Eleven states seceded from the Union and formed the Confederate States of America, 1860-1861.

1862 DAVID GLASGOW FARRAGUT WAS APPOINTED COMMANDER IN THE UNITED STATES NAVY AND SERVED IN THE WAR BETWEEN THE STATES.

President Abraham Lincoln delivered a famous address at Gettysburg, 1863.

The Emancipation Proclamation was issued, 1863.

President Lincoln was assassinated, 1865.

The Thirteenth Amendment to the Constitution, forbidding slavery, was ratified, 1865.

1866 FARRAGUT BECAME A FIRST ADMIRAL IN THE UNITED STATES NAVY.

The first Transatlantic cable was laid, 1866.

The United States purchased Alaska, 1867.

The first transcontinental railroad was completed, 1869.

1870   FARRAGUT DIED AT PORTSMOUTH, NEW HAMP-
SHIRE, AUGUST 14.

There were thirty-seven states in the Union.

Ulysses S. Grant was President, 1869-1877.

The population of the country was about
38,560,000.

DO YOU REMEMBER?

1. Where did James Glasgow Farragut live when the story begins?

2. Why did the Farraguts move to New Orleans?

3. What dangerous trip did James Glasgow take with his father across Lake Pontchartrain?

4. Why did James Glasgow go to live with Captain Porter after his mother died?

5. How did Captain David Porter help James Glasgow get a commission in the Navy?

6. What new name did James Glasgow get when he received his commission?

7. Why did David Glasgow have a fight one day with some boys on the shore at Norfolk?

8. What important message about war did Captain Porter read to the "Essex" crew?

9. How did Captain Porter frighten and subdue the British prisoners?

10. What troubles did the "Essex" crew have in rounding the Horn?

11. How did Mister Farragut become commander of the "Barclay" on a trip to Valparaiso?

12. How did the British ship, the "Phoebe," manage to capture the "Essex"?

13. How did Farragut happen to be chosen to command a blockading squadron during the War between the States?

14. How did Farragut capture New Orleans?

15. How did he help to capture Vicksburg?

16. How did he defeat the famous charm ship, the "Tennessee," in Mobile Bay?

17. What position did Farragut hold in the Navy after the War between the States?

IT'S FUN TO LOOK UP THESE THINGS

1. How old must a person be today to become a midshipman?

2. What was the Embargo Act which Congress passed during Jefferson's administration?

3. What was the cause of the War of 1812, or the Second War with England?

4. Where is New Orleans, and on what famous river is it located?

5. Why was the North eager to control the Mississippi River as soon as possible in the War between the States?

6. When were iron-clad or iron-covered ships first used in warfare?

INTERESTING THINGS YOU CAN DO

1. Find out what war vessels were like when Farragut first became a sailor.

2. Make a model or a drawing of a dugout canoe to show to the class.

3. Draw a map to show how the lower Mississippi River forms a delta.

4. Read to learn how ships formerly used flags and lights to signal one another.

5. Find out how the "Star-Spangled Banner" came to be written during the War of 1812.

6. Collect pictures of old warships for an exhibit on the bulletin board.

OTHER BOOKS YOU MAY ENJOY READING

David Farragut, Sailor, Ferdinand Reyher. Lippincott.

John Paul Jones: Salt-Water Boy, Dorothea J. Snow. Trade and School Editions, Bobbs-Merrill.

Panama Canal, The, Bob Considine. Trade Edition, Random House. School Edition, Hale.

Robert Fulton and the Steamboat, Ralph Nading Hill. Random House.

Stephen Decatur: Gallant Boy, Bradford Smith. Trade and School Editions, Bobbs-Merrill.

Story of Ulysses S. Grant, Jeannette C. Nolan. Grosset.

INTERESTING WORDS IN THIS BOOK

adios (ä thyōs′) : good-by (Spanish)

bantam (băn′tăm) : small fowl, always ready to fight

bowsprit (bou′sprĭt) : large masts extending forward from a vessel

buenos dias (bwĕ′nôs dē′äs) : good morning or good day (Spanish)

buenas noches (bwĕ′näs nô′chĕs) : good night (Spanish)

carronade (kăr ŭ nād′) : short, iron cannon

chantey (shȧn′tĭ) : song sung by sailors in rhythm with their work

davit (dăv′ĭt) : crane for hoisting boats or cargo

dogwatch (dŏg wŏch′) : watch for two hours on shipboard

freshet (frĕsh′ĕt) : stream overflowing

gig (gĭg) : long, light boat

hasta luego (äs′tä lōo ĕ′gô) : "See you soon" (Spanish)

hatchway (hăch′wā) : square opening in the deck of a ship leading to another deck

impress (ĭm prĕs′) : force into service in the navy

jib (jĭb) : triangular sail

ketch (kĕch) : sailing vessel similar to a yawl

larboard (lär′bōrd) : side of a ship on the left of a person facing the bow, or front

leeward (lē′wĕrd) : side of a ship away from or protected from the wind

marauding (mȧ rôd′ĭng) : roving about to plunder

199

midshipman (mĭd'shĭp'mǎn) : sailor ranking below a commissioned officer, nowadays from the Naval Academy

oakum (ō'kŭm) : loose fibers of old hemp ropes, used in mending seams in ships to prevent leaks

plum duff (plŭm dŭf') : plain pudding containing raisins or currants

quarter-deck (kwôr'tēr dĕk) : part of the upper deck used by officers

ruffle (rŭf''l) : low beat of the drum, not so loud as a roll

schooner (skōōn'ēr) : sailing vessel with two masts fore and aft

sea pie (sē'pī) : kind of pie made of meat and vegetables baked between two crusts

starboard (stär'bōrd) : side of a vessel on the right of a person facing the bow

weather side (wĕth'ēr sīd) : side of a ship most exposed to the weather

wherry (hwĕr'ĭ) : long, light rowboat, pointed at both ends

windward (wĭnd'wērd) : side of a ship toward which the wind blows

yard (yärd) : long, tapered mast, to support sails